EL Maths

Entry Level Mathematics 2-4

Gill Hewlett

Published in 2003 by:
Nelson Thornes Ltd
Delta Place
27 Bath Road
CHELTENHAM
GL53 7TH
United Kingdom

03 04 05 06 07 / 10 9 8 7 6 5 4 3 2 1

A catalogue record for this book is available from the British Library

ISBN 0 7487 7456 4

Illustrations by Mark Draisey

Page make-up by Tech Set Ltd

Printed and bound in Great Britain by Scotprint

CONTENTS

LEVEL 4

2.1 ADDING + SUBTRACTING

TALKING POINT

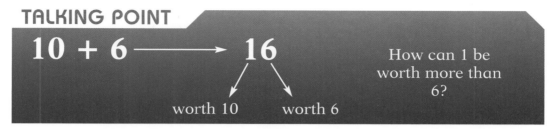

$$10 + 6 \longrightarrow 16$$

worth 10   worth 6

How can 1 be worth more than 6?

A Copy and complete these sums.

1 10 + 7 = ☐   4 60 + ☐ = 67   7 ☐ + 6 = 76
2 ☐ + 8 = 28   5 ☐ + 9 = 29   8 90 + ☐ = 92
3 30 + 5 = ☐   6 80 + ☐ = 81   9 50 + 3 = ☐

JUST DO IT!

Use your calculator. Which sum gives the highest answer?
Which sum gives the lowest answer?

27 + 32   41 + 11   35 + 21

Make up some sums of your own. Give them to a friend to find the highest and the lowest answer.

B Write down the *higher* number of each pair.

1 27, 36   3 74, 47   5 70, 68
2 42, 28   4 38, 62   6 19, 24

Write these numbers in order, *smallest* first.

7 22, 38, 24, 32   9 63, 36, 66, 34, 43
8 15, 87, 9, 28, 30   10 15, 5, 25, 52, 51

JUST DO IT!

Collect the house number of everyone in your class.
Write each one on a different card.
Put the cards in order and stick them on paper.

TALKING POINT

27
+18
───
35   ✗

Fiona

What has Fiona done wrong?

46
+28
───
74   ✓

Nikki

1

C Add these numbers. Write your workings in your book.

1	23 + 43	**4**	64 + 25	**7**	29 + 38
2	52 + 36	**5**	18 + 36	**8**	58 + 18
3	42 + 42	**6**	74 + 17	**9**	77 + 44

10	13 + 24 + 12	**12**	14 + 22 + 54	**14**	62 + 8 + 27
11	42 + 12 + 13	**13**	45 + 14 + 21	**15**	55 + 36 + 9

FACT

You can re-write a sum to help you. Like this:

Change 18 − 7 to

$$\begin{array}{r} \mathbf{t\ u} \\ 1\ 8 \\ -\ \ 7 \\ \hline 1\ 1 \\ \hline \end{array}$$

or

You can **subtract** by **adding on**. Try both.

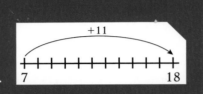

D Subtract these numbers. Write your workings in your book.

1	18 − 7	**4**	20 − 4	**7**	20 − 6
2	15 − 3	**5**	20 − 13	**8**	25 − 4
3	19 − 9	**6**	20 − 19	**9**	25 − 10

JUST DO IT!

Use a calculator to find out all the pairs of numbers that add up to 20. Write them down in order.

Here's one to start you off: 14 + 6 = 20

All these sums are connected.

12 + 8 = 20   20 − 12 = 8   20 − 8 = 12

E Write down the two missing sums for each question that are connected.

1	7 + 13 = 20	_____	_____
2	_____	20 − 4 = 16	_____
3	_____	_____	20 − 5 = 15

JUST DO IT!

Work with a friend.
You say a number in words. They write it down in numbers.
Take it in turns.
See who gets the most correct. (Choose numbers under 100!)

REVISION

FACT

28

worth 20   worth 8

You can re-write a sum to help you.

You can **subtract** by **adding on**.

All these sums are connected:

$17 + 3 = 20$ $20 - 3 = 17$ $20 - 17 = 3$

LEARNING TIPS

Write your own sums and find the answers. Check them on a calculator

Look at the numbers on the houses in your road. Check the pattern

Revise with a friend. Check each other's work

CHECK IT OUT

1   Copy and complete these sums.

   a ☐ $+ 4 = 24$ **b** $30 +$ ☐ $= 37$ **c** $40 + 6 =$ ☐

2   Write down the higher number in each pair.

   a 36, 24   **b** 48, 57   **c** 82, 28

3   Write these numbers in order, smallest first.

   a 36, 63, 24, 42   **b** 53, 47, 19, 28, 62, 26

4   Find the answers to these sums.

   a $27 + 13$ **c** $20 - 17$
   b $12 + 14 + 20$ **d** $25 - 3$

5   Write down the missing connected sums.

   _____ $20 - 1 = 19$ _____

2.2 PATTERNS

Valerie and Barbara are making necklaces from beads.

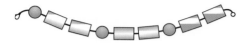

Valerie's necklace

The pattern is: red, blue, blue, red, blue, blue …

Barbara's necklace

The pattern is: blue, red, red, blue, red, red …

JUST DO IT!

Use beads, counters or linking cubes to make 'necklaces'.
Draw and colour each one.

A **1** Explain the difference between the pattern in Valeries necklace and Barbara's necklace.

2 Write down the pattern for each necklace.

a  **c**

b  **d**

> When numbers follow a pattern it is called a **sequence**.
> Each number is called a **term**.

FACT

B　Write down the next 5 terms for each sequence.

　　1　1, 2, 2, 1, 2, 2, 1, …

　　2　1, 2, 3, 1, 2, 3, 1, 2, …

　　3　1, 2, 3, 3, 1, 2, …

　　4　1, 3, 5, 1, 3, …

　　5　4, 4, 2, 4, …

　　6　2, 1, 6, 6, 2, 1, …

JUST DO IT!

Start with 4 on a calculator. Press + 2 = . Write down the answer. Do this 4 more times. You have made a sequence!

Make some more sequences.

Make a list of your sequences.

C　Find the missing shapes in these pattern sequences.

　　1　△ □ □ △ __ □ __ □ □ __

　　2　○ △ __ __ △ □ ○ △ □

　　3　□ ▣ ▣ ▣ __ □ □ __ ▣

　　4　__ | + ✳ □ | __ ✳ __ |

Copy each grid. Fill in the missing patterns.

5

□	⬡	
⊟	⬔	⬖
⊞	⬙	

6

A		C
B	A	B
	B	A

7

1		3
	$\frac{2}{2}$	$\frac{3}{2}$
$\frac{1}{3}$	$\frac{2}{3}$	

TALKING POINT

Is there more than one sequence that goes up in 2s?

Can you find a sequence that goes up in 10s?

D Write down how to find the next term for each sequence.

Find the next 3 terms for each sequence.

1 2, 4, 6, 8, …

2 5, 10, 15, …

3 10, 20, 30, 40, …

4 10, 12, 14, 16, …

5 30, 35, 40, 45, …

JUST DO IT!

Make a 10 by 10 square.

Fill in the numbers from 1 to 100.

Then start anywhere on the square. Write down the numbers.
Add on 5. Write down the new number. Write down 8 terms like this.
Try other starting numbers and add-on numbers.

E **1** Look at this table for subtraction.

$11 - 1 = 10$

$10 - 1 = 9$

$9 - 1 = 8$

$8 - 1 = 7$

a Write down the next 3 lines of the table.

b Look for and explain patterns in the table.

2 Look at this table for subtraction

$20 - 4 = 16$

$19 - 4 = 15$

$18 - 4 = 14$

$17 - 4 = 13$

a Write down the next 3 lines of the table.

b Look for and explain patterns in the table.

REVISION

When numbers follow a pattern it is called a **sequence**.
Each number is called a **term**.

LEARNING TIPS

Practise counting on by the same number

Look for patterns in a 100 square

Try clapping some of the sequences

CHECK IT OUT

1 Write the next 5 terms in this sequence.
3, 6, 3, 5, 3, 4, ...

2 Find the missing shapes in this sequence.

3 Explain how you find the next term for these sequences.
Find the next 3 terms.
a 10, 15, 20, 25, ...
b 8, 10, 12, ...

ANSWERS

1 3, 3, 3, 2, 3 **2** **3a** add 5 30, 35, 40
b add 2 14, 16, 18

2.3 MULTIPLYING AND DIVIDING

TALKING POINT

Did you know there is more than one way of multiplying?

Do you know the connection between multiplying and adding?

Can you think of occasions when you need to multiply?

A 5×6 is the same as $\underbrace{6 + 6 + 6 + 6 + 6}_{5} = 30$

You can do this on your calculator

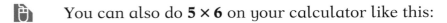

Work these out by adding.

1 $3 \times 4 = \underbrace{4 + 4 + 4}_{3} =$

2 $7 \times 2 =$

3 $5 \times 4 =$

4 $8 \times 4 =$

5 $6 \times 6 =$

6 $4 \times 6 =$

You can also do 5×6 on your calculator like this:

Work these out on your calculator.

7 $5 \times 4 =$ **12** $4 \times 9 =$

8 $5 \times 8 =$ **13** $8 \times 8 =$

9 $7 \times 4 =$ **14** $7 \times 6 =$

10 $4 \times 8 =$ **15** $3 \times 8 =$

11 $5 \times 7 =$

Multiplication is repeated addition.

FACT

β Choose a multiplication method to find out how much money there is in each pile.

1

four 20 p

4

eight 5 p

2

six 2 p

5

nine 1 p

3

seven 10 p

6

eight 10 p   four 2 p

JUST DO IT!

Make a money multiplication game.

You need a 10-sided dice.

Make cards with 1 p, 2 p, 5 p, 10 p and 20 p on them.

Turn them face down.

Turn one card over. Roll the dice.

Multiply the number on the dice by the money on the card.

Keep adding the total.

The first player to reach £2 wins.

| 1 p | 2 p | 5 p | 10 p | 20 p |

JUST DO IT!

Put **20** on your calculator. Keep subtracting **4** until you get 0.
It takes **5** turns.
You have just worked out:
$$20 \div 4 = 5$$

C Work these out by subtracting. You can use a calculator.

1 $12 \div 4 = \square$

$12 - \underbrace{4 - 4 - 4}_{3} = 0$

2 $20 \div 5 = \square$

$20 - 5 - 5 - 5 - 5 = 0$

3 $10 \div 2 =$

4 $15 \div 5 =$

5 $16 \div 4 =$

6 $27 \div 3 =$

7 $40 \div 5 =$

You can also find $20 \div 4$ on your calculator like this:

$$\boxed{2}\ \boxed{0}\ \boxed{\div}\ \boxed{4}\ \boxed{=}\qquad \boxed{5}$$

Work these out on your calculator.

8 $20 \div 2 =$

9 $9 \div 3 =$

10 $12 \div 3 =$

11 $30 \div 6 =$

12 $24 \div 6 =$

13 $18 \div 3 =$

14 $25 \div 5 =$

15 $35 \div 7 =$

16 $28 \div 4 =$

D Choose a division method to share money between friends.

1 £20 shared by 10 friends $\quad 20 \div 10 =$

2 £18 shared by 6 friends

3 £15 shared by 3 friends

4 £36 shared by 3 friends

5 £50 shared by 5 friends

6 £27 shared by 9 friends

JUST DO IT!

Find out what happens if you start with 100 and
a add 0
b multiply by 0
c subtract 0
d divide by 0.

What happens if you change 100 to another number?

FACT

Multiplication and **division** are connected.

All these sums are connected:

$$4 \times 5 = 20 \qquad 20 \div 4 = 5 \qquad 20 \div 5 = 4$$

E Write down the missing sums for each question.

1 $7 \times 3 = 21$ _____ _____

2 _____ $24 \div 4 = 6$ _____

3 $5 \times 8 = 40$ _____ _____

4 _____ _____ $12 \div 6 = 2$

JUST DO IT!

Work out the rule for finding the number in the square in each diagram.

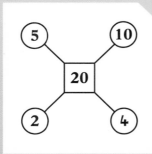
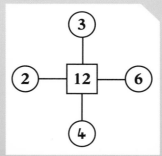

Find the missing numbers in these diagrams.

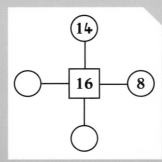
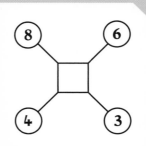

Make up some shape puzzles of your own.

REVISION

FACT

Multiplication is repeated addition.
Division is repeated subtraction.
All these sums are connected.

$$4 \times 7 = 28 \qquad 28 \div 4 = 7 \qquad 28 \div 7 = 4$$

LEARNING TIPS

Look for patterns in a times table square

Learn your 2, 5 and 10 times tables – get a friend to test you

Write out your 2, 5 and 10 times tables and pin them on your bedroom wall

CHECK IT OUT

Work these out by adding or multiplying.

1 $3 \times 8 =$ **2** $5 \times 5 =$ **3** $8 \times 2 =$

Find out how much money is in each pile.

4

seven 5 p

5

four 10 p

6

eight 2 p

Work these out by subtracting or dividing.

7 $8 \div 2 =$ **8** $32 \div 4 =$ **9** $27 \div 3 =$

Choose a division method to share money between friends.

10 £14 shared by 7 friends **11** £22 shared by 2 friends

Write down the missing sums.

12 $4 \times 6 = 24$ _____ _____

13 _____ $18 \div 6 = 3$ _____

2.4   MONEY

TALKING POINT

Do you know the new currency of France and Italy?
What is the currency of the USA?
Do you know the currency of Australia?

FACT

There are 100 pence in £1.
   100 p = £1

A   **1**   Write these amounts of money in order, smallest first.
   a 24 p, 17 p, 25 p, 19 p   **d** 5 p, £5, 15 p, 55 p, 50 p, £2.50
   b 68 p, 50 p, £1, 32 p, 45 p   **e** 76 p, 26 p, 52 p, 47 p, 33 p, 20 p
   c £2, £1.50, £5, £2.70, £2.90

2   Which sum gives the highest value?
   a 20 p + 15 p   *or*   10 p + 40 p?
   b 75 p − 10 p   *or*   50 p + 20 p?
   c 30 p + 25 p   *or*   70 p − 30 p?
   d 25 p + 25 p   *or*   75 p − 15 p?
   e 5 p + 10 p + 20 p   *or*   £1 − 50 p?

JUST DO IT!

Use the Internet to find out the year the UK went decimal.

Debbie and her mum are buying bargains.

6 items   2 items

6 × 10 p = 60 p   2 × 10 p = 20 p

BARGAIN BOX
EVERYTHING
10 p

B   **1**   Find out how much each person spends in the 10 p box.
   a Guru   – 3 items   **c** Claire – 7 items
   b Ramandeep – 4 items   **d** Sean   – 8 items

BARGAINS!
20p

MORE BARGAINS!
50p

2 Find out how much each person spends.
  a Peter buys 3 items at 20p each.
  b Holly buys 2 items at 50p each.
  c Sam buys 5 items at 20p each.
  d Angela buys 4 items at 50p each.
  e Ricki buys 6 items at 20p each.

JUST DO IT!

Frankie spent £1.10 on Chocs and Chews.

How many of each did he buy?

Chocs
20p

Chews
50p

Dave, Stuart and Steve go shopping.
Dave buys a canned drink for 35p.
He pays with a 50p coin.
He gets $50 - 35 = $ **15**p change.

C Find the change from 50p for each purchase.

1

snax
40p

4

ruler costs 42p

5
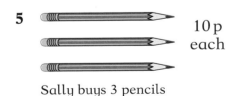
10p each

Sally buys 3 pencils

2

WHIZZ
45p

3
pen costs
22p

6

stamp costs
28p

7  bookmarks
20p
each

Gemma buys
2 bookmarks

8 erasers
6 p

Daniel buys
7 erasers

JUST DO IT!

Share 46 p between 3 people in a fair way.

What problems do you have?

How would you decide what to do?

JUST DO IT!

Use the Internet, or visit a bank, to find out how much money you need to open a bank account.

Is it the same for all banks?

W D Fill in this crossnumber.

1			2	3
		4		
	5			
6			7	
		8		

Across

1 12 p + 35 p

2 90 p − 16 p

5 £1 − 45 p

6 70 p − 27 p

8 Number of pence in £1.15

Down

1 10 × 4 p

3 Number of pence in £4

4 27 p + 38 p

5 73 p − 20 p

6 7 × 7 p

7 55 p ÷ 5

W E Follow these money trails and see
where you end up.

1 Adding 5 p

Start from the 5 p corner.
Follow the trail.
Add 5 p each time.
Where does the trail end –
corner A, corner B or corner C?

A

Start	5 p	15 p	20 p	70 p
5 p	7 p	35 p	40 p	65 p
10 p	15 p	30 p	45 p	50 p
25 p	20 p	25 p	50 p	65 p
70 p	65 p	60 p	55 p	70 p

C   B

W

2 Subtracting 2 p

Start from the 30 p corner.
Follow the trail.
Subtract 2 p each time.
Where does the trail end –
corner A, corner B or corner C?

A   B

8 p	14 p	16 p	10 p	8 p
10 p	12 p	18 p	20 p	14 p
12 p	26 p	24 p	22 p	20 p
30 p	28 p	22 p	24 p	10 p
Start	30 p	28 p	14 p	8 p

C

3 Make a money trail puzzle of your own

JUST DO IT! £ £ £ £ £ £ £ £

£ Find out how much the richest person in the UK earns
a year.

£ What is the biggest ever win on the lottery?

£ £ £ £ £ £ £ £ £ £ £

REVISION

There are 100p in £1.

100p = £1

LEARNING TIPS

Get hold of piles of money – and count them!

Look at the price of sweets. Work out the cost of two packets in your head

Write lists of money and add them up. Check your answers with a calculator

CHECK IT OUT

1   Write these amounts of money in order, smallest first.

42p, 48p, 34p, 41p, 49p, 36p

2   Which sum gives the higher value?

25p + 35p   *or*   70p − 25p?

3   Work out the cost of each of these.
   a 3 items at 20p   **c** 4 items at 10p
   b 8 items at 5p   **d** 3 items at 50p

4   Find the change from a 50p coin.

   a   **b**

35p

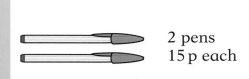

2 pens
15p each

2.5 NUMBER PROBLEMS

1 Tariq has 40 p. Jake has 24 p.
   a How much money do they have altogether?
   b How much more money does Tariq have?

2 The elephant is walking towards the bridge.

The elephant is 3 metres tall.

The bridge is 5 metres high.

How much spare room does the elephant have?

3

This stick of rock is 40 centimetres long.
5 friends share it equally. How long is each piece?

4 Lauren has this money in her pocket.
Which coins would she use to buy these?

   a

45 p

   b

Popstars mag

£1.15

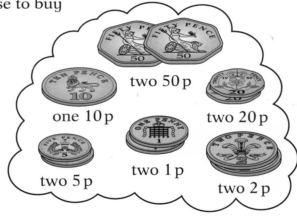

two 50 p

one 10 p   two 20 p

two 5 p   two 1 p

two 2 p

   d Has she got enough money to buy a £1.50 game?

   e How much money has she got altogether?

   c

6 p

5 a Which of these numbers appear in the 5 times table?
      25   40   17   32   15   14   20

   b Write down a rule for numbers in the 5 times table.

6 Every time Zac gets to school on time he puts 2 p in a jar.
  a How much has he got after one week?
  b How much has he got after 20 days?
  c How long will it take him to get £1?

7 How many 10p coins are there in this pile?

How much is this altogether?

8 Copy the diagram.
Fill in four numbers to make the sums work.

$$17 - \square = \boxed{10} = \square \div 2$$

$$3 + \square = \boxed{10} = 2 \times \square$$

Make up some sums of your own.

9

KINGS UNITED	V	QUEEN CITY
54		**2**

  a How many goals were scored altogether?
  b How many more goals did Kings United score?

JUST DO IT!

In a football match 7 goals were scored.
Find all the possible final scores.

JUST DO IT!

Choose two football teams. Find the results of all their matches this season.
Which team has scored the most goals?
What is the difference between the two totals?

10 Sherri is giving away her old CDs.
She has 18 CDs.
3 friends share them equally.
How many do they have each?

CLASSICAL

SOUNDS OF
THE 80S

2.6 FRACTIONS

You have to split things into equal parts to find **fractions**.

There are 4 equal parts for $\frac{1}{4}$ or $\frac{3}{4}$.

A Write down the number of equal parts for each fraction.

1 $\frac{1}{2}$ **3** $\frac{2}{3}$ **5** $\frac{1}{3}$ **7** $\frac{3}{5}$

2 $\frac{3}{4}$ **4** $\frac{2}{5}$ **6** $\frac{4}{5}$ **8** $\frac{1}{4}$

9 How can you tell how many equal parts by looking at the fraction?

W Split each shape into the correct number of equal parts.

10 $\frac{1}{4}$

11 $\frac{1}{5}$

12 $\frac{1}{3}$

13 $\frac{1}{2}$

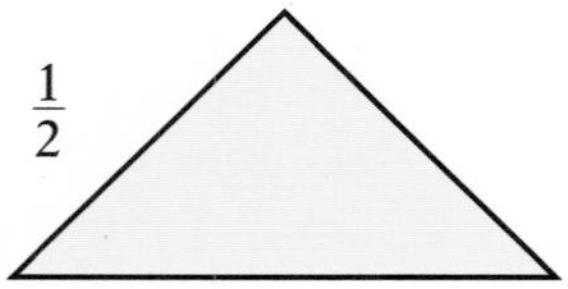

> The top of the fraction tells you **how many of the equal parts you need**.
>
> $\frac{3}{4}$
>
> | 1 | 2 |
> |---|---|
> | | 3 |

B How many equal parts do you need for each fraction?

1 $\frac{1}{2}$	**3** $\frac{2}{3}$	**5** $\frac{1}{3}$	**7** $\frac{3}{5}$
2 $\frac{3}{4}$	**4** $\frac{2}{5}$	**6** $\frac{4}{5}$	**8** $\frac{1}{4}$

Colour each shape to make the correct fraction.

9 $\frac{1}{4}$

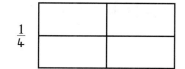

12 $\frac{1}{2}$

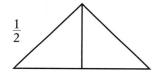

10 $\frac{1}{5}$

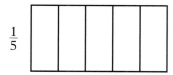

13 $\frac{3}{4}$

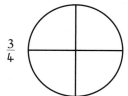

11 $\frac{1}{3}$

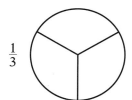

14 $\frac{3}{4}$

JUST DO IT!

Is half your class male and half female?

Is half your school male and half female?

Are half your teachers male and half female?

Is half your family male and half female?

C 1 Write down 'True' or 'False' for each sentence.
Write the correct sentence if the answer is 'False'.

    a To find $\frac{1}{2}$ you split into 3 equal parts.

    b To find $\frac{1}{5}$ you split into 5 equal parts.

    c To find $\frac{3}{4}$ you split into 3 equal parts.

    d To find $\frac{2}{3}$ you split into 3 equal parts.

    e You need 3 of the parts for $\frac{3}{4}$.

    f You need 2 of the parts for $\frac{2}{5}$.

    g You need 2 of the parts for $\frac{1}{2}$.

    h To find $\frac{3}{5}$ you split into 5 equal parts.
Then you need 3 of the parts.

  2 Write a sentence of your own for $\frac{4}{5}$.

  3 Write a sentence of your own for $\frac{1}{7}$.

JUST DO IT!

1 Get 20 counters.

2 Split them into 4 equal parts:

3 Put 3 piles together. Count the counters. Did you get 15?

   $\frac{3}{4}$ of 20 = 15

D Use counters to find these fractions of numbers.

   1 $\frac{1}{2}$ of 10   **3** $\frac{1}{5}$ of 10   **5** $\frac{4}{5}$ of 20

   2 $\frac{3}{4}$ of 12   **4** $\frac{1}{4}$ of 16   **6** $\frac{3}{4}$ of 28

JUST DO IT!

Choose any method to find out who has more money:

Richard has $\frac{3}{4}$ of £32

Lee has $\frac{1}{2}$ of £40

Write some fraction questions for a friend.

Hint: Use counters for £s.

E 1 Kiri has £24. She gives $\frac{1}{2}$ to her brother Luke. How much does Luke have?

  2 Hugh and Richard share £40. Hugh has $\frac{3}{4}$ and Richard has $\frac{1}{4}$. How much does each boy have?

  3 Why can't you find half of the players in a football side?

REVISION

You have to split things into equal parts to find **fractions**. The **bottom** number tells you **how many equal parts**:

$$\frac{3}{4}$$

The **top** number tells you **how many parts you need**:

$$\frac{3}{4}$$

You can use counters to help find fractions of numbers.

LEARNING TIPS

Look at bars of chocolate. Look at the chunks. Work out the fractions

Try cutting round cakes or pizzas into EXACT quarters

Find out why an American quarter is called a 'quarter'

CHECK IT OUT

1   Write down the number of equal parts for $\frac{1}{5}$.

2   Copy this shape. Split it into equal parts for $\frac{1}{5}$.

3   Copy this shape. Colour the fraction $\frac{3}{4}$.

4   Find: **a** $\frac{1}{2}$ of 8   **b** $\frac{3}{4}$ of 12   **c** $\frac{2}{5}$ of 10.

5   Find: **a** $\frac{1}{4}$ of £40   **b** $\frac{2}{5}$ of £20.

2.7 LANGUAGE OF NUMBER

1	one	6	six
2	two	7	seven
3	three	8	eight
4	four	9	nine
5	five	10	ten

JUST DO IT!

Work in pairs.
Take it in turns to roll a 10-sided dice.
Write down the number as a word.
Check the spelling.
One point for each correct spelling.

First to 5 points wins the game.

W A Fill in the missing letters for each word.

1 9 n i __ e

2 6 s __ x

3 8 e i __ h t

4 4 f __ u r

5 3 __ __ r e e

6 1 o __ e

7 Jumble the missing letters to make a word.

10	ten	60	sixty
20	twenty	70	seventy
30	thirty	80	eighty
40	forty	90	ninety
50	fifty	100	one hundred

B Write down the answer to each question in words.

1 20 + 30

2 80 − 10

3 4 × 20

4 70 + 30

5 40 + 50

6 100 − 40

7 30 − 10

8 2 × 30

Write these numbers in words.

9 44

10 22

11 55

12 130

13 33

14 67

15 27

16 98

17 88

TALKING POINT

Petra and Chloe are looking for words that rhyme with numbers:

Eight   rhymes with   **gate**

8

C   Write down as many words as you can that rhyme with each number.

1 Use a dictionary to check the spellings.

a	Three	3	**f**	Seven	7
b	Two	2	**g**	Nine	9
c	Five	5	**h**	Four	4
d	Ten	10	**i**	Six	6
e	Eighty	80	**j**	Twenty	20

W D   Find the words in the Numbers wordsearch.

Numbers

```
I   D   E   S   E   N   O   H
S   E   V   E   N   T   Y   U
T   P   I   V   W   F   T   N
T   E   F   E   X   I   H   D
O   H   N   N   X   F   G   R
Y   T   R   I   H   T   I   E
Y   Z   S   E   T   Y   E   D
T   N   I   N   E   T   Y   J
```

EIGHT	EIGHTY	FIFTY
FIVE	HUNDRED	NINE
NINETY	ONE	SEVEN
SEVENTY	SIX	TEN
THIRTY	THREE	TWENTY

JUST DO IT!

Make posters and learn the different words that mean the same.

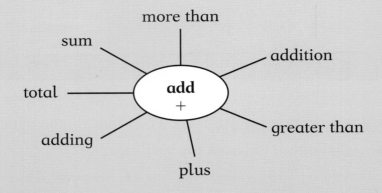

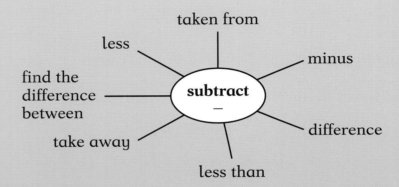

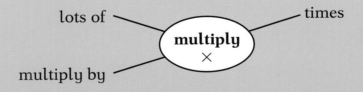

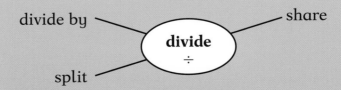

Find other words that mean the same.

W E Complete this Mega Number Puzzle.

Mega Number Puzzle

Across

3 A quarter is one of these
4 A tree with an h in it
7 Numbers that divide by 2 are this
9 The number half way between two and six
10 Used to work out sums
12 A longer word for add
13 Ten and ten more
16 Make up an hour
17 How many tens in twenty?

Down

1 Money that is worth less than a pound
2 The correct word for share
5 Forty plus sixty
6 Another word for add
8 Made up of twenty-four hours
9 5 multiplied by ten
11 Used to buy things
14 Thirty plus sixty
15 A number that rhymes with hen

REVISION

LEARNING TIPS

Look, cover, write, check to learn spellings

Look for words that look the same to help learn spellings

Learn *key* words

CHECK IT OUT

Can you:

1   spell the numbers 1 to 10, 20, 30, 40, 50, 60, 70, 80, 90 and 100?

2   recognise words that mean add, subtract, multiply and divide?

2.8　PLACE VALUE

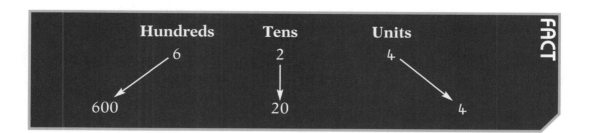

Hundreds	Tens	Units
6	2	4
600	20	4

A　Write down the value of the 3 in each number.

1	13	4	341	7	340
2	38	5	73	8	483
3	123	6	235	9	832

JUST DO IT!

1　Play in pairs.
　　Make grids like this.
　　You need one each.

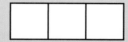

2　Take it in turns to roll a 10-sided dice.

3　Choose where to place the number on *your* grid.

4　Roll the dice 3 times each.

5　The person with the highest number on their grid wins.

Claudine and Marlene rolled a 2, then an 8, then a 7.

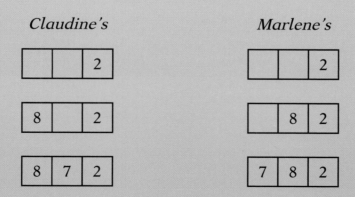

Claudine's　　　　　*Marlene's*

Claudine wins!

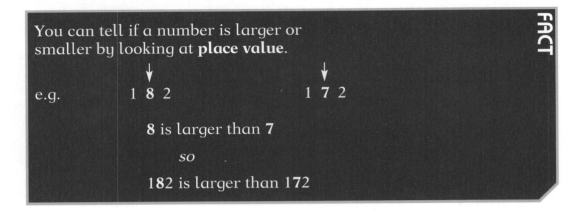

You can tell if a number is larger or smaller by looking at **place value**.

e.g.   1 **8** 2   1 **7** 2

            8 is larger than **7**

                    so

            182 is larger than 172

FACT

B Write down which number is larger.

1	127, 147	**4**	539, 589	**7**	347, 387
2	38, 78	**5**	41, 40	**8**	255, 225
3	204, 224	**6**	292, 222	**3**	100, 106

C Find the difference between each pair of numbers.

1	38 and 68	**4**	652 and 642
2	104 and 74	**5**	242 and 222
3	525 and 585	**6**	775 and 755

7 Write the answers to questions **1** to **6** in order, smallest first.

Write down 2 numbers with each of these differences.

8	10	**10**	50	**12**	80	**14**	30
9	40	**11**	70	**13**	20	**15**	100

TALKING POINT

What is the smallest number you have ever come across?
What is the largest number you have ever come across?
Can you write them down in words and numbers?

JUST DO IT!

Try putting a very large number on your calculator. Find out what happens.

REVISION

FACT

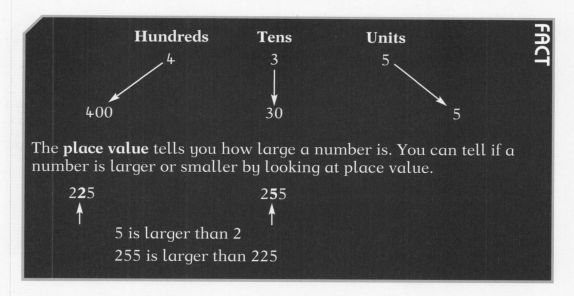

The **place value** tells you how large a number is. You can tell if a number is larger or smaller by looking at place value.

225   255

↑   ↑

5 is larger than 2
255 is larger than 225

LEARNING TIPS

Look at a till receipt. Explain why some amounts are longer than others

Find out the biggest amount of money in the lottery in Ireland and in America?

Say these numbers:

1
12
123
1234

See how far you can go

CHECK IT OUT

1   Write down the value of the 7 in each number.
    a 27   **b** 724   **c** 375

2   Write down which number is larger.
    373   *or*   333

3   Find the difference between 585 and 525.

4   Write down 2 numbers with a difference of 40.

2.9 USING SYMBOLS

TALKING POINT

Where do you see symbols in everyday life?

Do you always know what they mean?

Symbols can be used when you don't know a number.

FACT

A Find the value of the symbol in each sum.

1 $3 + ✳ = 5$

2 $8 - \square = 6$

3 $5 \times ❖ = 10$

4 $18 \div \diamondsuit = 6$

5 $20 - 18 = $

6 $14 \div 2 = \square$

7 $\triangle \times 4 = 20$

8 $\triangleright + 5 = 12$

JUST DO IT!

Find the 'symbols' window in Word.

Choose 12 symbols and make a symbols leaflet.

In a question the same symbol always stands for the same number.

FACT

B Find the value of each symbol.

1 $\otimes + \otimes + \otimes + \otimes = 12$

2 $\otimes + \square = 10$

3 $\square + \square = 14$

4 $\square - \triangle = 5$

5 Make up some sums using $\square$, $\otimes$ and $\triangle$

JUST DO IT!

The Egyptians used symbols for numbers and words.

Find the Egyptian symbols for the numbers up to 100. Find out what they were called.

Write some sums using Egyptian symbols.

FACT

The Romans used letters for numbers. We call them **Roman numerals**:

$$D = 500 \qquad L = 50$$

$$M = 1000 \qquad C = 100 \qquad X = 10 \qquad V = 5 \qquad I = 1$$

$$MD = 1500 \qquad XV = 15$$

C Write down these Roman numerals as numbers.

1	VI	**4**	XXIII	**7**	DLX
2	XII	**5**	DX	**8**	LXI
3	CXX	**6**	DL	**9**	MDCLXVI

JUST DO IT!

You can work out the year a TV programme is made by watching the credits as they roll at the end of the programme.

The year is shown in Roman numerals.

Work out the year your favourite TV programmes were made.

Some codes use numbers for letters of the alphabet.

A	B	C	D	E	F	G	H	I	J	K	L	M
1	2	3	4	5	6	7	8	9	10	11	12	13

10 Make a chart of number codes for all the letters in the alphabet.

Work out what each number code means.

11

3	15	4	5

12

14	21	13	2	5	18

13

19	5	22	5	14

14	20	23	5	14	20	25	

15	1	4	4	9	20	9	15	14

16	6	18	1	3	20	9	15	14

Write each word in code.

17 EIGHT

18 PLUS

19 MULTIPLY

20 EVEN

21 THIRTY

22 SYMBOLS

JUST DO IT!

Write a message to a friend. Change it to number code and ask them to work it out.

JUST DO IT!

Braille is a way of writing so that blind people can read. They read by feeling 'bumps' on paper.

Find out how to write the alphabet in Braille.

Use alphabet code to find the answer to each sum. Write the answer as a letter.

23 $Z - K = \boxed{}$

24 $M - A = \boxed{}$

25 $J + E + C = \boxed{}$

26 $L \times B = \boxed{}$

27 $X \div D = \boxed{}$

28 $N - I + K = \boxed{}$

REVISION

FACT

Symbols can be used when you don't know a number.
The Romans used letters for numbers.
Some codes use numbers for letters.

CHECK IT OUT

Find the value of the symbols in each sum.

1   ◤ + 8 = 20

2   ❀ + ❀ + ❀ = 12

3   28 ÷ 4 = △

4   ❀ + ⊗ = 5

2.10 SHAPES

TALKING POINT

Do you know the difference between a flat shape and a solid shape?

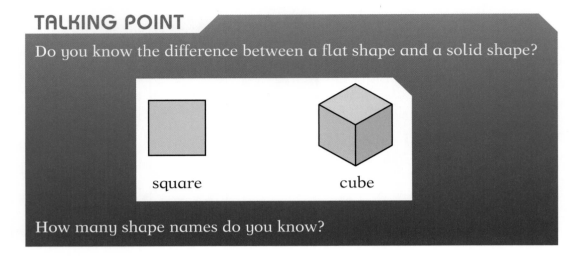

square   cube

How many shape names do you know?

Triangles have 3 straight sides and 3 **vertices** (corners).
Pentagons have 5 straight sides and 5 vertices.

FACT

A **1** Sort these shapes into 3 groups: triangles, pentagons, neither.

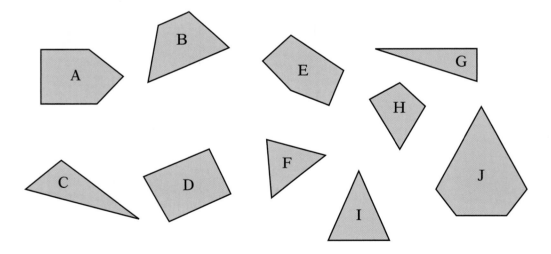

2 Draw 3 pentagons using a pencil and ruler.

3 Draw 3 triangles using a pencil and ruler.

4 Draw 3 shapes with straight sides that are *neither* triangles *nor* pentagons.

> **FACT**
>
> **Quadrilaterals** all have 4 straight sides and 4 vertices.

B **1** Which of these shapes are quadrilaterals?

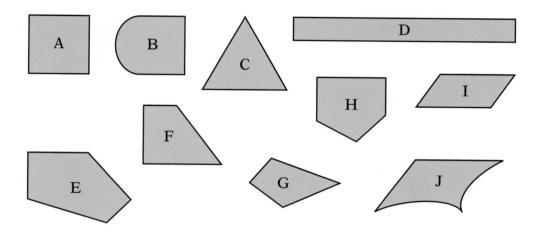

JUST DO IT!

What are the special names of
a a six-sided shape
b an eight-sided shape?

How many other names of shapes can you find?

W **2** All these triangles fit together to make a quadrilateral.

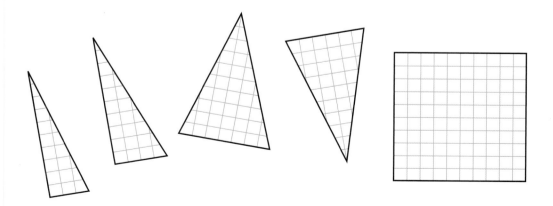

Use the worksheet to make the quadrilateral.

C Look at each shape. Write down how many sides and vertices each shape has. Write the name of the shape.

1

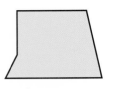

sides =
vertices =
name = _____

4

7

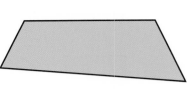

2

5

8

3

6

9

A **cuboid** is a **solid** shape.

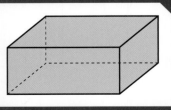

It has 8 vertices.

It has 12 edges.

It has 6 faces.

FACT

D Write down the number of vertices, edges and faces for each solid shape.

1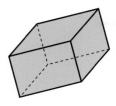

vertices =
edges =
faces =

3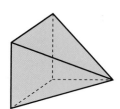

5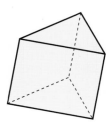

2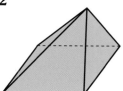

4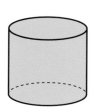

6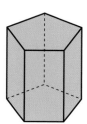

E For each shape write down whether it is flat (plane) or solid.

1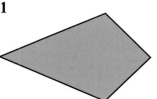

3

5

2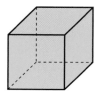

4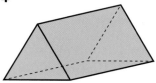

6

REVISION

FACT

Triangles have 3 straight sides and 3 **vertices**.
Quadrilaterals have 4 straight sides and 4 vertices.
Pentagons have 5 straight sides and 5 vertices.
A **cuboid** is a **solid** shape.

LEARNING TIPS

Picture each shape in your mind with the name inside it

Find other words that begin with PENT, HEX, QUAD, TRI. This helps you learn how many sides each shape has

CHECK IT OUT

1 Say whether each shape is a triangle, quadrilateral, pentagon or none of these.

a   b   c   d

2 How many sides and vertices does this shape have?

4 Write down whether each shape is plane or solid.

a   b

3 How many vertices, edges and faces does this solid have?

2.11 CHANGING SHAPES

A 1 Some of these └ shapes are the same. They have been moved into different positions.

Use tracing paper to find out which ones are the same as the blue └ .

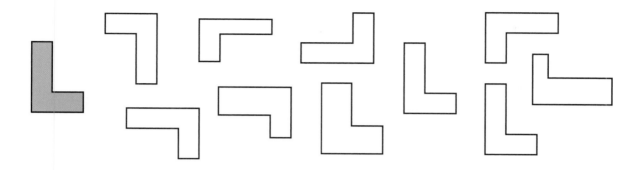

2 Find which X are the same as the green X.

3 Find which ☆ are the same as the yellow ☆ .

JUST DO IT!

You can find pictures and symbols on the computer in Word.

Increasing the font size enlarges the picture:

Log on to Word.

Use the toolbar to **Insert**. Then choose **Symbol**.

Choose some symbols.

Insert the symbols into a blank document.

Enlarge the symbols by increasing the font size.

ß

1 This pattern is made by turning the shape. It is turned by the same amount every time.

Draw the next three arrows.
They must follow the pattern.

2

Draw the next three shapes in the pattern.

3

Draw the missing shape and the next three shapes in the pattern.

4

Draw the missing shape and the next three shapes in the pattern.

JUST DO IT!

Print some symbols from Word or use the Worksheet.

Cut out the symbols.

Make your own patterns by turning a symbol by the same amount each time.

FACT

This is an **analogue** clock. The hands turn **clockwise**.

In a *quarter of an hour* both hands have turned.
The *minute* hand has turned a quarter of the way around the clock.
The *hour* hand has turned a quarter of the way between 4 and 5.

W C **1** Use a clock face worksheet. Draw the position of the hands of the
clock a quarter of an hour *after* these times.

a

e

i

b

f

j

c

g
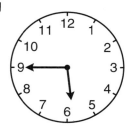

k

d
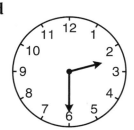

h

l
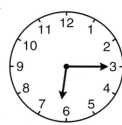

2 Draw the positions of the hands of the clock a quarter of an hour *before* these times.

a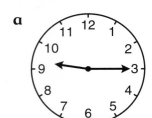

b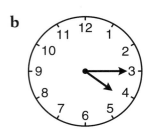

c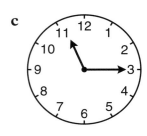

d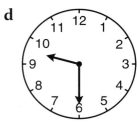

e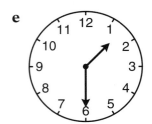

f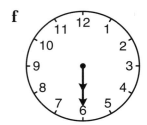

g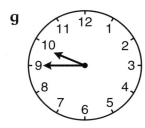

h

i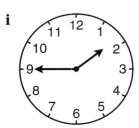

j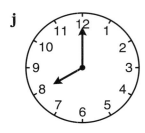

k

l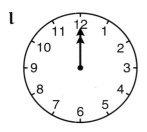

JUST DO IT!

Give directions to your friend or teacher to get from one corner of the room to another.

Use left, right and straight on.

REVISION

LEARNING TIPS

Look for turning patterns in wallpaper and fabric	Use tracing paper to check if shapes are the same	Practise drawing shapes and turning them

CHECK IT OUT

1 Which of these shapes are the same?

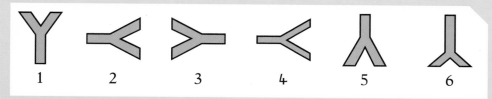

2 Draw the next 3 shapes in this turning pattern.

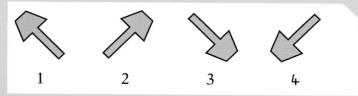

3 a Draw the position of the hands of the clock a quarter of an hour *after* this time:

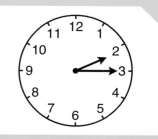

b Draw the hands on this clock a quarter of an hour *before* this time:

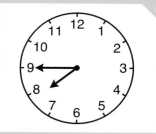

ANSWERS

1 2, 3 and 5

2

3a

b

2.12 TIME

Kaylie is first in the 200 m.
Her winning time
is 28 seconds.

00:28 00

This is a
digital
stopwatch

This is an
analogue
stopwatch

A   Write down the times on each of these stopwatches.

1

00:45 00

4

7

00:55 00

2

5

00:30 00

8

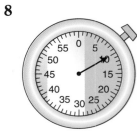

3

6

00:25 00

9

JUST DO IT!

Use a stopwatch to find out how long you can hold your breath.

What happens to the stopwatch display after one minute?

B   **1**   Write down the times on each analogue clock.

a

e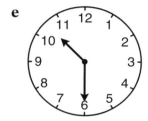

i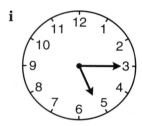

b

f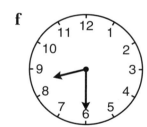

j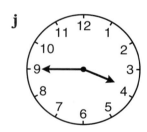

c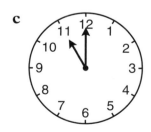

g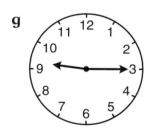

k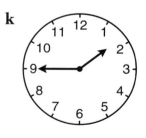

d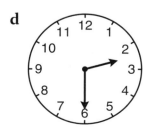

h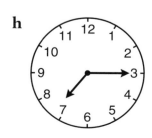

l

2 Write down the times on each digital clock.

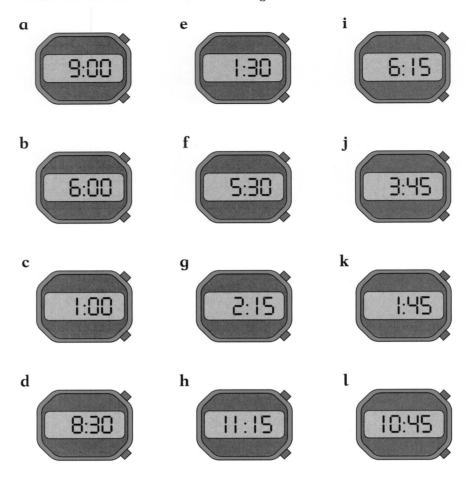

a 9:00

b 6:00

c 1:00

d 8:30

e 1:30

f 5:30

g 2:15

h 11:15

i 6:15

j 3:45

k 1:45

l 10:45

3 Match the analogue and digital clock times.

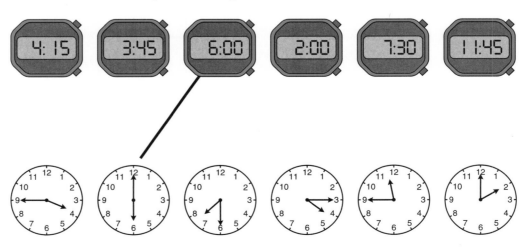

4:15   3:45   6:00   2:00   7:30   11:45

4 Show these times on analogue clocks.

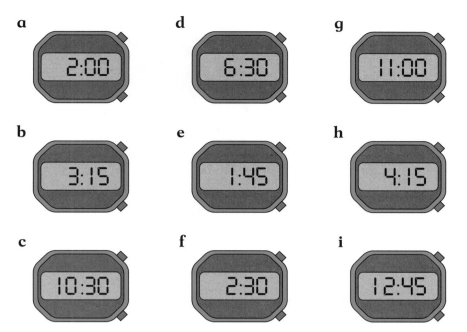

a 2:00

d 6:30

g 11:00

b 3:15

e 1:45

h 4:15

c 10:30

f 2:30

i 12:45

5 Show these times on digital clocks.

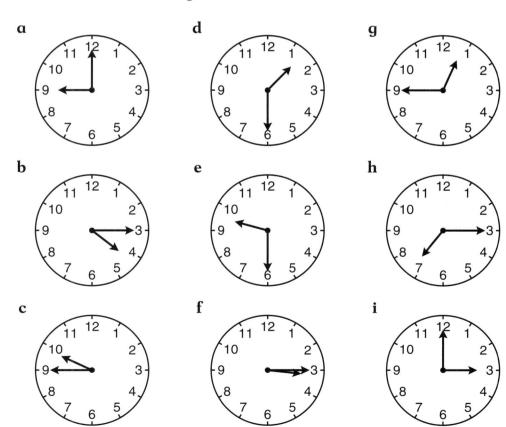

In the bakery, bread is ready every 5 minutes.

C **1** Write down the next 3 times bread will be ready.

7:00

7:05

7:10

2 For each question, write down the next 4 times bread will be ready.

a 3:20
   3:25

c 5:30
   5:35
   5:40

e 11:40
   11:45
   11:50

b 1:45
   1:50
   1:55

d 2:05
   2:10
   2:15
   2:20

f 7:10

JUST DO IT!

You need a 6-sided dice.
Play this with a friend.

1 Write down a digital time.

2 Roll the dice.

3 Your friend has to add on 5 minutes to your time once for every number on the dice. For example, a throw of 3 means add on $3 \times 5 = 15$ minutes.

4 Take it in turns to roll the dice/add on times.

You can change the game by taking off time instead of adding it on. You can change from 5 minutes to 10 minutes.

This is 3 o'clock
in the morning.

This is 3 o'clock
in the afternoon.

To tell the difference, use **am** for morning and **pm** for afternoon.

1 2 3 4 5 6 7 8 9 10 11 12 1 2 3 4 5 6 7 8 9 10 11 12

←——————— am ——————→←—————— pm —————→ am

1 2 3 4 5 6 7 8 9 10 11 12 13 14 15 16 17 18 19 20 21 22 23 24

Digital clocks use 1: to 24:

2 am is 2:00   **11 pm is 23:00**

D Use the scale to match the times.

1 4 am = _____   **7** 23:00 = _____

2 1 pm = _____   **8** 4:00 = _____

3 2 am = _____   **9** 11:00 = _____

4 2 pm = _____   **10** 14:00 = _____

5 10 pm = _____   **11** 3:00 = _____

6 6 am = _____   **12** 17:00 = _____

REVISION

FACT

You can read time **digitally** and using **analogue** clocks
Time can be shown using **am/pm** or **24 hours**.

LEARNING TIPS

Practise reading the time every 5/10 minutes by saying the time out loud

Look at clocks when you are in town or at the leisure centre

Find the difference in times by adding on

CHECK IT OUT

1 Write down the time on each stopwatch.

a

b

2 Write down the time on each clock.

a

b

c

d

3 Sally is adding 5 minutes each time. Write down the next 3 times.
7:20, 7:25, 7:30, 7:35 _____ _____ _____

4 **a** Write 4 pm using the 24-hour clock.
b Write 11:30 using am or pm.

2.13 SYMMETRY

FACT

Symmetry means 'the same'.

This shape has **reflection symmetry** –
one side is the same as the other
when it is reflected.

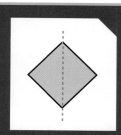

This shape is **symmetrical**.
It has *one* line of symmetry.

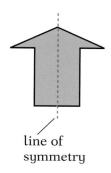

line of
symmetry

A

1 Draw the line of symmetry on each shape or picture.

a

d

g

b

e

h

c

f

This shape has *no* lines of symmetry.

It has **rotation** symmetry because you can turn it and it looks the same in two positions.

2 Match each shape with the number of positions it looks the same as it is rotated.

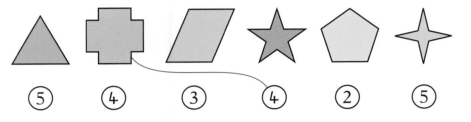

⑤   ④   ③   ④   ②   ⑤

JUST DO IT!

You can use mosaic patterns that are symmetrical

Find Roman or Greek mosaic patterns on the Internet.

Draw your own mosaic using centimetre squared paper.

Use colours that the Romans or Greeks would have used.

Make sure your mosaic has *reflection symmetry* or *rotation symmetry*.

1 Write down the next two numbers in each pattern.
  a 2 4 2 4 2
  b 1 2 3 1 2 3
  c 5 5 4 5 5 4 5
  d 3 7 3 7 3 7
  e 2 10 10 10 2 10 10 10

2 Draw the next two shapes in each pattern.

  a △ ■ △ ■ △ ■
  b ○ ○ △ ○ ○ △
  c ⬠ ⬠ ⬠ ○ ⬠ ⬠
  d † † † † † †
  e ★ ✪ ✪ ✪ ★ ✪

REVISION

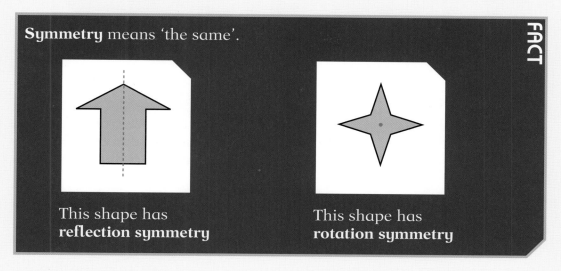

Symmetry means 'the same'.

FACT

This shape has
reflection symmetry

This shape has
rotation symmetry

LEARNING TIPS

Check if shapes have reflection symmetry by folding

Check if shapes have rotation symmetry by turning

CHECK IT OUT

1 Draw the line of symmetry on this shape.

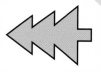

2 This shape has rotation symmetry. Match the shape with the number of positions it looks the same.

2?   3?   4?

3 a Write down the next 2 numbers in this pattern: 4 6 6 4 6

b Draw the next 2 shapes in this pattern: ○ ○ + + ○

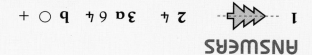

ANSWERS

1 ⟪← 2 4 3a 6 4 b ○ +

55

2.14 DRAWING SHAPES AND RIGHT ANGLES

You can use a pair of compasses to draw circles.

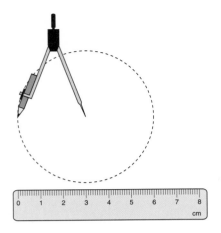

The distance from the centre of the circle to the edge is called the **radius**.

A **1** Draw these circles. Open the compasses to these measurements.
- **a** radius 3 cm
- **b** radius 4 cm
- **c** radius 25 mm
- **d** radius 35 mm.

JUST DO IT!

On a piece of A4 paper draw these 12 circles.
Make them overlap:

4 circles with radius 5 cm
4 circles with radius 4 cm
4 circles with radius 3 cm

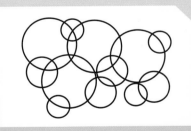

Now colour in the picture using only 4 colours. Try not to have two sections next to each other the same colour.

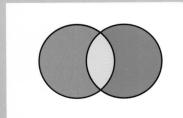

You can use a pair of compasses and a ruler to draw triangles:

1 side with a ruler.
2 sides with compasses and a ruler.

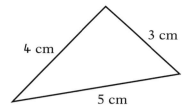

Draw one side with the ruler. Make it exactly 5 cm long.

Open the compasses to 4 cm
and draw an arc on the paper,
from one end of the line.

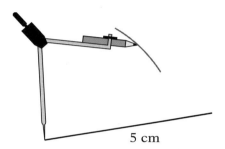

Open the compasses to 3 cm
and draw an arc from the other
end of the line. Make it cross
the first arc.

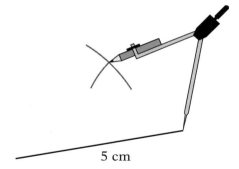

Use a ruler to join the 5 cm
line to the point where the
arcs cross. Do not rub out
your arcs.

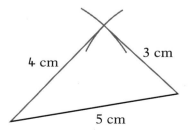

2 Draw these triangles using a ruler and a pair of compasses.

a

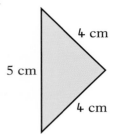

4 cm

5 cm

4 cm

c

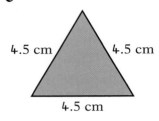

4.5 cm   4.5 cm

4.5 cm

b

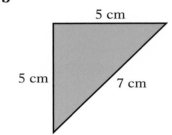

5 cm

5 cm   7 cm

d

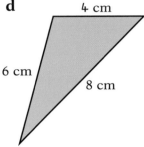

4 cm

6 cm

8 cm

3 Use card or paper for this question.
Draw 4 equilateral triangles joined together.
Draw the blue triangle first.
Then draw the red lines.

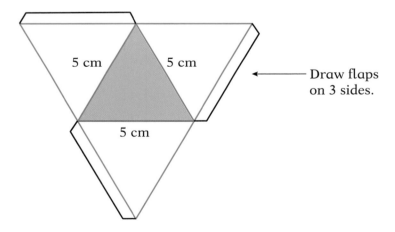

5 cm   5 cm

5 cm

Draw flaps
on 3 sides.

Cut out the shape and fold it.
Make a triangular-based pyramid.
This is called a tetrahedron.

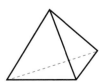

An **angle** is the measurement between two lines.

A **right angle** is a corner.

This window has 4 right angles, one at each corner.

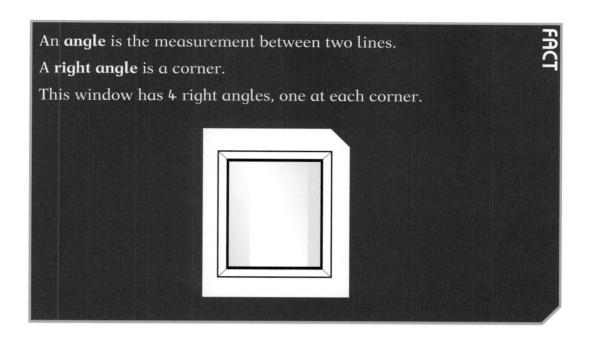

FACT

B **1** For each angle write down whether it is smaller or larger than a right angle.

a

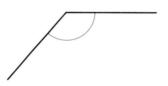

d

b

e

c

f

2 Write down 'right' or 'not right' for each angle by looking – no measuring!

a

d

g

b

e

h

c

f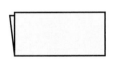

i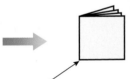

JUST DO IT!

You can make a right angle.
Fold a piece of paper in half and in half again.

This is a right angle

You can use this to measure angles.

3 For each angle write down whether it *is* a right angle or *is not* a right angle.

a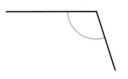

c

e

b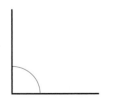

d

f

REVISION

The distance from the centre of a circle to the edge is called the **radius**.

An **equilateral triangle** has 3 sides of equal length.

You can make a **right angle** by folding a piece of paper in half and then in half again.

LEARNING TIPS

Draw two lines to make an angle. Estimate whether it is larger or smaller than a right angle. Use folded paper to check

Practise drawing circles in different patterns – try to draw a target

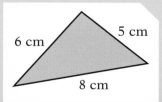

CHECK IT OUT

1 Draw a circle with radius 40 mm.

2 Draw this triangle accurately with a ruler and compasses.

6 cm   5 cm   8 cm

3 Write down whether each angle is smaller than, larger than or is a right angle.

   a   b   c   d

2.15 WEIGHING AND MEASURING

TALKING POINT

Do you know if something weighs one kilogram *without* actually weighing it?

Does this book weigh more or less than one kilogram?

<	>	kg
less than	**more than**	**kilogram**

A **1** Write down whether each of these weighs more than (>) one kilogram or less than (<) one kilogram.

  a 5 CDs   **e** 3 videos

  b A pair of trainers   **f** A computer printer

  c A bicycle   **g** 20 mobile phones

  d A skateboard   **h** A basketball

JUST DO IT!

Use scales to help you learn to judge weights.

Weigh: 1 kg of newspapers
  1 kg of pens/pencils
  1 kg of mobile phones
  1 kg of trainers

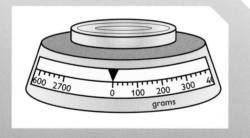

B **1** Use a metre stick to help you estimate whether each item is less than or more than one metre.

  a The height of a desk.

  b The height of a door.

  c The width of a bed.

  d The height of a bicycle.

  e Three of your paces.

  f The distance or height you can jump.

2   Use a ruler to measure each line.

a   _____

b   _____

c   _____

d   _____

e   _____

f   _____

g   _____

h   _____

3   Jaye and her friends are buying ribbon for their textiles coursework. Each piece measures 10 cm.

Write down how much ribbon Jaye buys altogether if she buys:

     a   3 pieces   **c**   4 pieces   **e**   2 pieces
     b   6 pieces   **d**   9 pieces   **f**   7 pieces

4   **a**   Rebecca buys 40 cm of ribbon. How many 10 cm pieces does she buy?

     b   Martyn buys 80 cm of ribbon. How many 10 cm pieces does he buy?

     c   Tom buys 20 cm of ribbon. How many 10 cm pieces does he buy?

     d   Helen buys 50 cm of ribbon. How many 10 cm pieces does she buy?

     e   Adam buys 70 cm of ribbon. How many 10 cm pieces does he buy?

C   **1**   Put these measurements in order, smallest first.

     a   17 cm,   22 cm,   9 cm,   36 cm
     b   40 cm,   60 cm,   20 cm,   50 cm
     c   12 cm,   24 cm,   13 cm,   20 cm
     d   7 cm,   27 cm,   17 cm,   32 cm
     e   22 cm,   12 cm,   18 cm,   19 cm

2 Measure the sides of each triangle and pentagon.

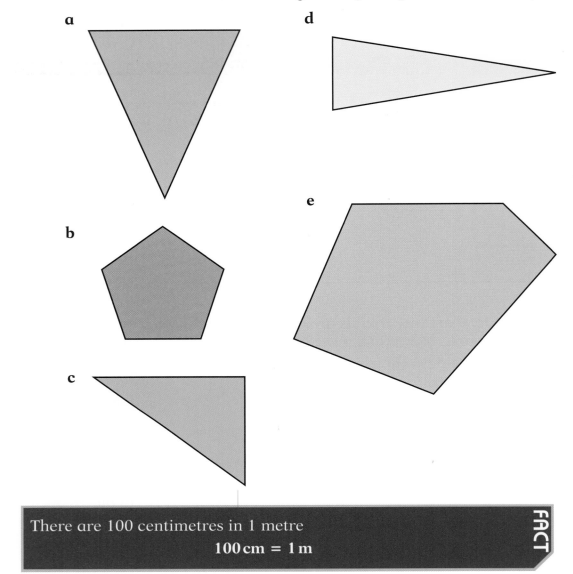

a

d

e

b

c

There are 100 centimetres in 1 metre

100 cm = 1 m

FACT

JUST DO IT!

You need: a 1 metre stick or tape
          several 30 cm rulers

Find out how many 30 cm rulers make 1 metre. Is it an exact number?

3 Put these measurements in order, smallest first.
   a 2 m, 8 m, 3 m, 10 m
   b 5 m, 14 m, 3 m, 10 m
   c 8 m, 3 m, 5 m, 9 m
   d 20 m, 10 m, 12 m, 11 m
   e 15 m, 9 m, 7 m, 12 m

REVISION

FACT

> means **greater than**   < means **less than**

cm means **centimetre**

m means **metre**

100 cm = 1 m

LEARNING TIPS

Always start reading your ruler at 0

Practise measuring. Try to estimate how long something is before you measure

CHECK IT OUT

1 Write down which weighs more than 1 kilogram and which weighs less than 1 kilogram.
  a a portable CD player   **b** a chair

2 Measure this line _____

3 How many pieces of 10 cm ribbon make 50 cm?

4 Put these measurements in order, smallest first.
  a 20 cm, 18 cm, 9 cm, 19 cm
  b 13 m, 4 m, 8 m, 5 m

2.16 SHAPE, SPACE AND MEASURE PROBLEMS

1   Terri has arranged to meet her friends in the shopping centre at 4 o'clock.
It takes her 20 minutes to get there.
How long does she have before she has to leave?

2   The time in Moscow is 3 hours ahead of the time in the UK. What time is it in Moscow when it is 14:30 in the UK?

3 **a** Write down the name of this shape.

    b Can you draw 2 straight lines on the shape and end up with 3 triangles?

4   This box is a cuboid.
Look at the measurements.

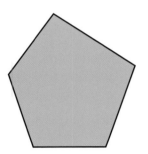

Work out how many cubes can fit in the box.

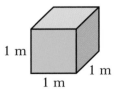

5   Which solid has more vertices, a cube or a pyramid?

6   How many times does the minute hand point to a number in two hours?

7 Write two sets of instructions using 'Turn right', 'Turn left' and 'straight on' to get through this maze.

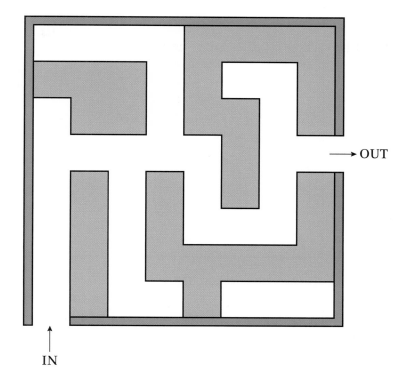

8 How could you change this shape to make it have reflection symmetry? Draw the new shape.

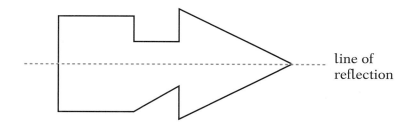

line of reflection

W

9 How many times can you fit this shape into a square measuring 6 cm by 8 cm?

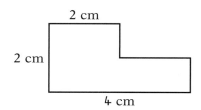

2 cm

2 cm

4 cm

10   This piece of modern art is made from 6 plane shapes.

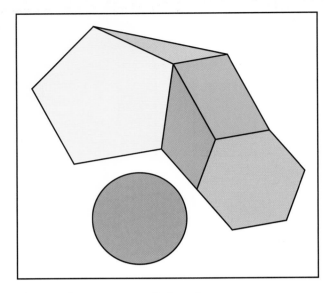

    a Write down the names of the shapes.
    b Draw a piece of modern art using the following shapes:
      2 squares   2 triangles
      1 circle   1 pentagon.

11   Harry has some rods of different lengths

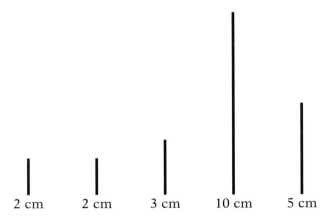

2 cm   2 cm   3 cm   10 cm   5 cm

Work out which of these lengths he can make by joining rods together.

a ——————————— 15 cm   **e** ————— 11 cm

b ——— 4 cm   **f** ——————— 12 cm

c ———— 6 cm   **g** ——————————— 20 cm

d ————— 8 cm   **h** ——————————— 17 cm

2.17 THE LANGUAGE OF SHAPE, SPACE AND MEASURE

A Re-arrange the letters to find shape words.

1

C
I   C
L   R
E

_ _ _ C _ _

2

E
S   Q
U   A
R

_ _ U _ _ _

3

R
L   A
I   T
E   N
G

_ _ I A _ _ _ E

4

C
T   G
A   N
O   O

_ _ _ _ _ _ _

5

T
P   A
O   G
N   E
N

_ E _ _ _ _ _ _

6

B
C   E
U

_ _ _ _ _

7

X
N   A
E   H
G   O

_ _ _ _ _ _ _

W **B**   Choose a word starter, a word ending and a meaning.
Write a sentence for each one.
This is an example:

word starter   word ending   meaning
hex   agon   means any
                                           6-sided shape

JUST DO IT!

Find as many words as you can that end with gram.

_____gram

C   Write down the word for each clue. The numbers tell you how many letters in the answer.

1   60 seconds is the same as this. (6)

2   A type of symmetry. You could use a mirror. (10)

3   85 is _____ 22. (4, 4)

4   There are 24 in a day. (5)

5   Fruit and vegetables are weighed in these. (9)

6   This shape has 5 sides. (8)

7   Use these to draw circles. (9)

8   The distance from the centre of a circle to the edge. (6)

JUST DO IT!

Make up crossword clues for these words.

DIGITAL

RECTANGLE

SOLID

ENLARGEMENT

Choose extra words of your own.

D

1	2	3	4	5	6	7	8	9	10	11	12	13
Y	Z	A	B	C	D	E	F	G	H	I	J	K

14	15	16	17	18	19	20	21	22	23	24	25	26
L	M	N	O	P	Q	R	S	T	U	V	W	X

Use the code to find each of these words.

1 | 7 | 6 | 9 | 7 |

2 | 21 | 19 | 23 | 3 | 20 | 7 |

3 | 5 | 14 | 17 | 5 | 13 |

4 | 20 | 23 | 14 | 7 | 20 |

5 | 10 | 7 | 26 | 3 | 9 | 17 | 16 |

Write these words in code.

6 ROTATION

7 SYMMETRY

8 KILOGRAM

9 TRIANGLE

10 LESS THAN

JUST DO IT!

Use the letter code to play this game.

Each player makes a maths word that has a high score. The highest score wins 1 point.

The first player to get 5 points wins.

2.18 SORTING

TALKING POINT

Are you a tidy person?

How often do you tidy
your bedroom?

Is it a good thing to be tidy?

W A   **1** Sort these different footwear
into boots, shoes and trainers.

boots	shoes	trainers

W   **2** Sort these clothes into coats,
trousers and shirts.

coats	shirts	trousers

3 Sort these numbers into numbers ending in 3, numbers ending in 0 and numbers ending in 7.

27   13   20   23   33   17   40

ending in 3	ending in 0	ending in 7

4 Sort these shapes into 3-sided shapes, 4-sided shapes and 5-sided shapes.

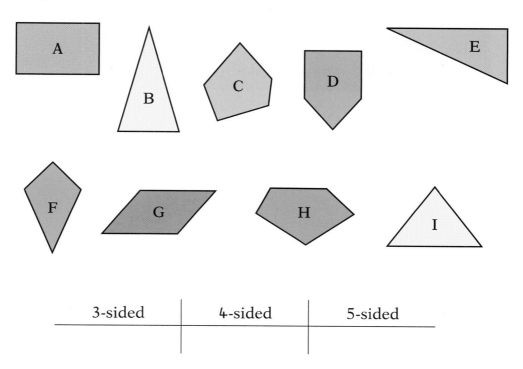

3-sided	4-sided	5-sided

5 Sort these words into 3-letter words, 4-letter words and 5-letter words.

even   sum   take   level

add

odd   minus   plus

3 letters	4 letters	5 letters

W **JUST DO IT!**

Cut out the colour and shape cards.
Shuffle the cards and put them face down.

First game
Turn the cards over and sort them into colours.

Second game
Turn the cards over and sort them into shapes.

Use the blank card sheet to make some sorting cards.

Choose numbers, shapes or colours.

B **1** Sam has sorted some numbers.

_____	_____	_____
2 22	15 25	36 16
32	45	26

a Write down the headings for Sam's table.

b Write all the numbers in a list. Put them in order, smallest first.

2 Charlotte has sorted some shapes.

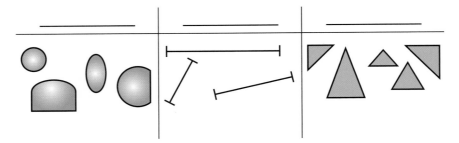

a Write down the headings for Charlotte's table.

b Which column has most shapes?

c Which column has least shapes?

3 Shoehi has sorted some toys.

  a Write down the headings for each column.
  b Which category has the most items?
  c Which category has the least items?

4 Christian has sorted some equipment.

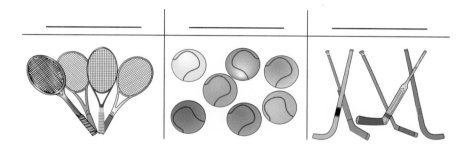

  a Write down the headings for each column.
  b Which category has the most items?
  c Which category has the least items?

5 Rachael has sorted some objects.

  a Write down the headings for each column.
  b Which category has the most items?
  c Which category has the least items?

JUST DO IT!

Modern car registration numbers are made up like this:

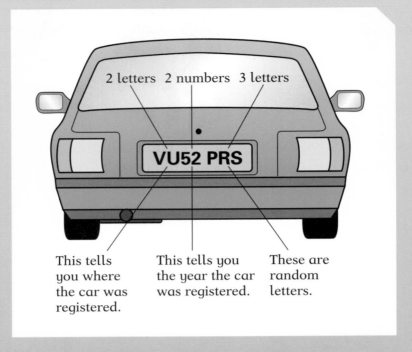

2 letters   2 numbers   3 letters

VU52 PRS

This tells you where the car was registered.

This tells you the year the car was registered.

These are random letters.

1   Use the Internet or a car magazine to find out how many different places cars can be registered.
    Write or print off a list.

2   Find out how you can tell which year a car was registered by looking at the number.

3   Look out for car registration numbers and work out where they were registered and how old they are.

4   Different countries have different national identification letters for cars.
    Match the countries with their letters.

GB   Great Britain
USA   Ireland
D   United States of America
IRL   Germany
F   France

Tables can be used to sort things into **categories**.

LEARNING TIPS

Try sorting buttons in more than one way

Sort out your school books and files

Use a number square and colour in all the numbers that have the same ending number

CHECK IT OUT

1   Sort these different containers into boxes, cans or bottles.

boxes	cans	bottles

A   B   C   D   E   F   G   H

2   Write down the headings for Maddy's table.

41 91	74 14	27 67
1 31	24	47

2.19 COLLECTING DATA

JUST DO IT!

Ask everyone in your class if they are happy, sad or neither.
Put your results in a tally-chart like this.

happy	||||	5
sad	|||	3
neither	||||	4

The **information** you collect is called **data**.

FACT

TALKING POINT

Why do you need to record your results in a table?

Which of these two tally methods is easier to count?

Method 1

\|\|\|\|\|\|\|\|\|\|\|\|\|\|

Method 2

\|\|\|\| \|\|\|\| \|\|\|\|

1 Write each number as a tally.

   a 2   **c** 4   **e** 12   **g** 15

   b 5   **d** 8   **f** 9   **h** 21

2 Write each tally as a number.

   a \|\|\|\| \| **d** \|\|\|\| **g** \|

   b \|\|\| **e** \|\|\|\| \|\| **h** \|\|\|\| \|\|\|\| \|\|\|\| \|\|\|

   c \|\|\|\| \|\|\|\| **f** \|\|\|\| \|\|\|\| \|

3   Re-write these tallies using the correct method.

   a | | | | | | **e** | | | | | | | | | | | |

   b | | | | | | | | | | **f** | | | | | | | | | | | | | |

   c | | | | | | | | | **g** | | | | | | | | | | | | | | | | | | | |

   d | | | | |

JUST DO IT!

Make up your own categories to tally using
a 6-sided dice.

Choose how many times to roll the dice.

Make it into a game and play with a friend.

Dice Game

β   **1**   You need a 6-sided dice.
         Roll the dice 12 times.
         Record your results in a tally-chart like this.

Numbers 1–3		
Numbers 4–6		

2   You need a 6-sided dice.
       Roll the dice 20 times.
       Record your results in a tally-chart like this.

Numbers 2, 4, 6		
Numbers 1, 3, 5		

3 You need a 6-sided dice.
Roll the dice 24 times.
Record your results in a tally-chart like this.

Numbers 1, 2, 6		
Numbers 3, 4, 5		

W C Each person in Mike's class has collected some data.
Put the data into a tally-chart.

1

happy	sad	sad	neither	neither	happy	happy
sad	happy	happy	sad	sad	neither	

happy		
sad		
neither		

W

2 Everyone's favourite colour:

red	blue	black	black	red	red	red
red	blue	black	red	red	red	black

red		
blue		
black		

JUST DO IT!

Throw a coin 10 times.
Record how many heads and how many tails you get in a tally-chart like this:

Heads	Tails
ⅢⅢ I	IIII

Now throw a coin 20 times.
Do you get twice as many heads and twice as many tails?

REVISION

FACT

The **information** you collect is called **data**.
You use **tallies** to count data.
You record results in a **tally-char**t.

LEARNING TIPS

Practise your 5 times table to help you count in fives

Cross off each piece of data with a pencil so you don't count it twice

CHECK IT OUT

1   Write each number as a tally.
    a 4   **b** 12

2   Write each tally as a number.

    a 卌 || **b** 卌 卌 |||

3   Write this tally using the correct method.

    |||||||||||

4   Put this data into a tally-chart.

green	green	blue	yellow	green	green
blue	blue	yellow	green	green	blue
yellow	green	yellow	green	blue	blue
green	green	yellow	green	green	blue

green		
blue		
yellow		

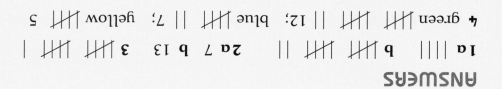

81

2.20 TABLES

Can you read a bus or train timetable?

Can you find the table of ingredients on a cereal box?

Can you find a table in newspaper TV listings?

Where else is information put in tables?

A   This is Davina's school timetable.

	1	2	Break	3	4	Lunch	5
M	PE	Science Lab 4 Miss Peters		English Room 19 Mrs Brown	English Room 19 Mrs Brown		Maths Room 8 Mr Limb
T	ICT Room 15 Mr Wood	Maths Room 8 Mr Limb		Science Lab 4 Miss Peters	Geography Room 12 Mr Thomas		Technology Workshop A Mrs Phillips
W	Geography Room 12 Mr Thomas	Technology Workshop B Mrs Kay		Maths Room 8 Mr Limb	Technology Workshop C Mr Smith		Science Lab 4 Miss Peters
Th	Science Lab 4 Miss Peters	Technology Workshop B Mrs Kay		ICT Room 15 Mr Wood	Form Time Room 12		PE
F	Geography Room 12 Mr Thomas	Maths Room 8 Mr Limb		English Room 19 Mrs Brown	English Room 19 Mrs Brown		Science Lab 4 Miss Peters

1   a How many times does Davina have maths in one week?

   b What is the name of her maths teacher?

   c Which room does she have maths in?

   d Which day doesn't Davina have maths?

2   a Which is the only subject that has a double lesson?

   b Which is the only subject that Davina has more than one teacher for? How many does she have?

   c Davina has her form time in the same room as one of her subjects. Which one?

3 Write down the subject for each lesson.
   a Tuesday lesson 4
   b Monday lesson 1
   c Friday lesson 3
   d Wednesday lesson 2
   e Thursday lesson 5

4 Write a list of every subject Davina has on her timetable and how many times she has it.

JUST DO IT!

Make up your own 'Perfect School Timetable'
How many PE lessons would you include?
Which subjects would you include that you don't do now?
Make a display with illustrations that match your timetable.
Explain why your timetable is perfect.

TALKING POINT

Have you got a mobile phone?

What make is your phone?

What is the most popular phone in your class?

Is it cheaper to pay-as-you-go or have a contract?

B This table shows how much each person spent on mobile phone calls in January.

January phone calls

Name	Cost (£)
Jade	5
Amy	10
Kylie	5
Shane	20
Farid	0
Daniel	15
Jason	5
David	10
Maddy	10
Ria	25
Kirsty	5
Kelly	15

1 Which person spent the most?
2 Which person spent the least?
3 How many people spent £5?
4 How many people spent £20?
5 How many people spent £10?
6 How much did Farid spend?
7 Who spent more, David or Kirsty?
8 Who spent less, Kylie or Maddy?
9 How much did Kelly and Daniel spend altogether?
10 Which boy spent the most?

This table shows how much each person spent on mobile phone calls in February.

11 Which person spent the most?
12 Which person spent the least?
13 How many people spent £5?
14 How many people spent £20?
15 How many people spent £10?
16 How much did Farid spend?
17 Who spent more, David or Kirsty?
18 Who spent more, Kylie or Maddy?
19 Did Jade spend more or less in February?
20 Write down all the people who spent less in February.

February phone calls

Name	Cost (£)
Jade	10
Amy	10
Kylie	10
Shane	5
Farid	0
Daniel	15
Jason	5
David	15
Maddy	10
Ria	5
Kirsty	20
Kelly	15

This table shows information about Apple Core Mobile phone rates

21 How much is a peak rate local call per minute?
22 How much is an off-peak National call per minute?
23 How much is a local weekend call per minute?

		Pence per minute
Peak calls	Local	20 p
	National	20 p
Off-peak calls	Local	10 p
	National	15 p
Weekend calls	Local	5 p
	National	10 p

JUST DO IT!

Do you send text messages to your friends?
How could you write this text message in as few letters as possible?
'Will you be at the park tonight?'
Can you write a text message that someone can understand using only 5 letters or less?

REVISION

Information is often written in **tables**.

LEARNING TIPS

Keep a record of your mobile phone bills over a year to see how much you spend

Read the table of ingredients on the side of food packaging to see if you are eating healthily

Learn to use a bus or train timetable

CHECK IT OUT

1 This is part of Sean's timetable.

   a What lesson does Sean have in Lab 8?
   b Which teacher teaches in Room 6?
   c Who does Sean have for English?
   d Which subject does Mr Tray teach?

	1	2	3	Break	4
Mon	English Room 8 Mr Smith	Technology Lab 8 Miss Danks	Science Room 4 Mr Tray		Maths Room 6 Miss Patel
Tues	Maths Room 6 Miss Patel	Science Room 4 Mr Tray	English Room 8 Mr Smith		Technology Lab 8 Miss Danks
Wed	Geography Room 7 Mrs Feltz	Maths Room 6 Miss Patel	Technology Lab 8 Miss Danks		English Room 8 Mr Smith

2 This table shows mobile phone costs in March.

   a Which person spent the most?
   b Which person spent the least?
   c Who spent £10?
   d How much did Jade and Kylie spend altogether?

March phone calls

Name	Cost (£)
Jade	15
Amy	5
Kylie	20
Shane	10
Farid	0
Daniel	10
Jason	5

2.21 BAR-CHARTS AND PICTOGRAMS

Frequency means how many.

A Amber collected data from 10 people in her class. She puts the results in bar-charts.

1 **a** How many had blue eyes?

b How many had brown eyes?

c How many had neither blue nor brown eyes?

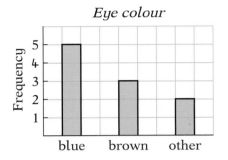

Eye colour

2 **a** How many wore size 10 trainers?

b How many wore size 8 trainers?

c How many wore size 6 trainers?

d Which was the most common size?

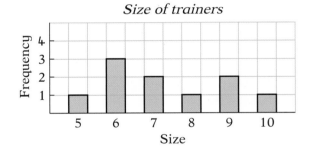

Size of trainers

3 **a** How many people had 1 mobile phone?

b How many more people had 1 mobile phone than 3 mobile phones?

c How many people had 4 mobile phones?

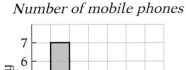

Number of mobile phones

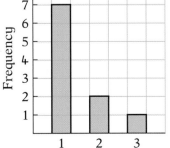

4 **a** How many people walked
to school?

b How many people travelled
to school in a vehicle?

c How many more people walked
to school than caught the bus?

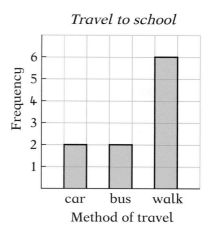

Travel to school

TALKING POINT

What are the names of the lines that make
the graph?

Did you know that every graph should have
a title?

What other types of graphs do you see in
newspapers?

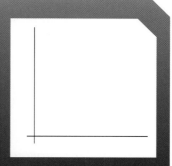

B The students at Clandon High School collected some data from their
classmates.

1

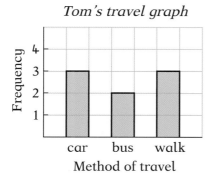

Tom's travel graph

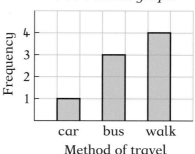

Joe's travel graph

a How many people walked to school in Tom's survey?

b How many people walked to school in Joe's survey?

c Who had more people travelling to school by bus?

d How many people were there in Tom's survey?

e How many people were there in Joe's survey?

2

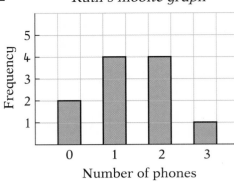

Ruth's mobile graph

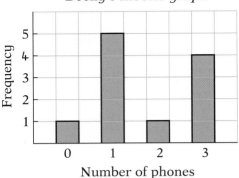

Becky's mobile graph

a How many people in Ruth's survey had 2 mobile phones?

b How many people in Becky's survey had 2 mobile phones?

c Which two categories had the same frequency in Ruth's survey?

d Which two categories had the same frequency in Becky's survey?

e How many people were there in Ruth's survey?

f How many people were there in Becky's survey?

3

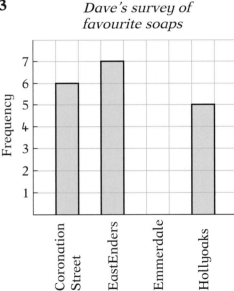

Dave's survey of favourite soaps

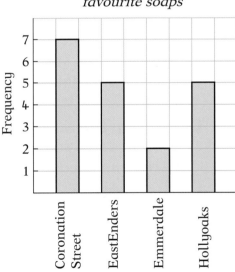

Mahesh's survey of favourite soaps

a Which was the most popular soap in Dave's survey?

b Which was the most popular soap in Mahesh's survey?

c Which was the least popular soap in Dave's survey?

d Which was the least popular soap in Mahesh's survey?

e How many people were there altogether in Dave's survey?

f How many people were there altogether in Mahesh's survey?

g Who asked the most people 'what is your favourite soap?'?

JUST DO IT!

Find out how to draw a bar-chart using Excel.

C Sue collected data from 10 people in her class. She put the results in pictograms.

1

Eye colour

blue	👁 👁 👁 👁 👁
brown	👁 👁
other	👁 👁 👁

Key: 👁 represents one person

a How many people had blue eyes?
b How many people had brown eyes?
c How many people had neither blue nor brown eyes?

2

Make of mobile

Sony	📱 📱 📱 📱 📱 📱
Nokia	📱 📱 📱
Motorola	📱

Key: 📱 represents one person

a Which was the most popular mobile?
b How many people owned a Sony mobile?
c How many more people owned a Nokia than a Motorola?

3

Favourite soap

Coronation Street	📺 📺 📺
EastEnders	📺 📺 📺 📺 📺 📺
Emmerdale	📺

Key: 📺 represents 1 person

a Which was the most popular soap?
b How many more people preferred EastEnders than Coronation Street?
c How many people preferred Coronation Street to Emmerdale?

4

Favourite ice cream flavour

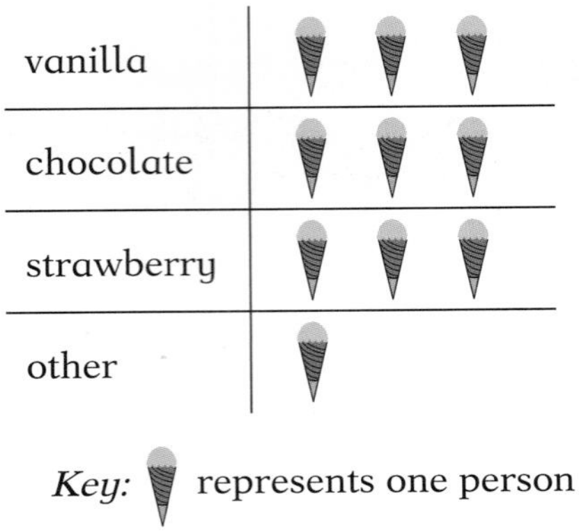

vanilla	
chocolate	
strawberry	
other	

Key: represents one person

a How many people preferred vanilla?

b Which flavours were chosen by the same number of people?

5 The cinema owner asked people their favourite type of film as they entered the cinema.

Favourite type of film

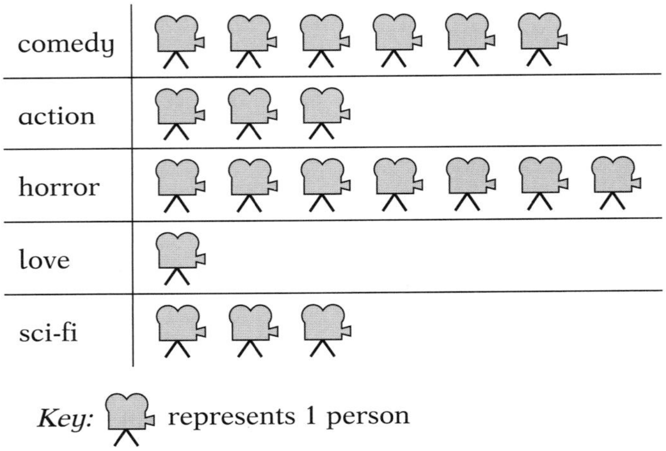

comedy	
action	
horror	
love	
sci-fi	

Key: represents 1 person

a Which was the least popular type of film?

b Which was the most popular type of film?

c Which two types of films were chosen by the same number of people?

d How many people did the cinema owner ask altogether?

REVISION

LEARNING TIPS

Make sure the bars on your bar-chart are the same width and evenly spaced

Always label the axes on a graph

The symbols on your pictograph should be the same size and be lined up

CHECK IT OUT

1 **a** Which was the most popular flavour of ice cream?
   b How many people liked vanilla or chocolate the most?
   c How many people were there in the survey?

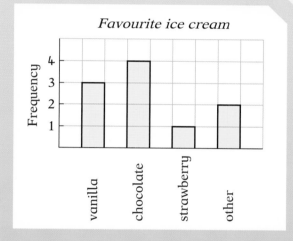

Favourite ice cream

2 **a** What was the most popular drink?
   b Which 2 drinks had the same results?
   c How many people were there in the survey?

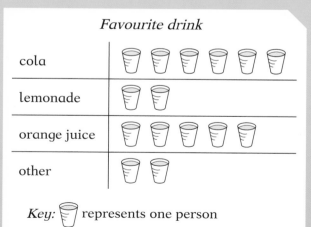

Favourite drink

cola

lemonade

orange juice

other

Key: 🥤 represents one person

1a chocolate **b** 7 **c** 10   **2a** cola **b** lemonade and other **c** 15

ANSWERS

2.22 PROBABILITY

TALKING POINT

Do you know what the weather will be like tomorrow?
Can you be certain?

Do you know what you will do tomorrow?
Can you be certain?

Do you know what you will be doing when you are 30?
Can you be certain?

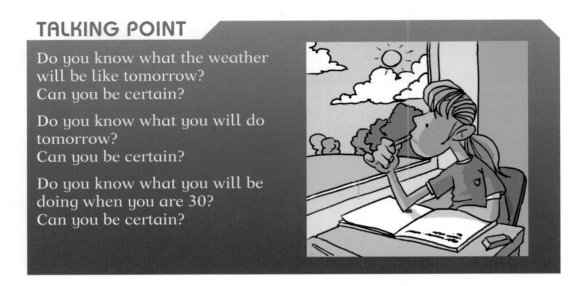

W A   **1**   Use a roadway marked in 10 year divisions.

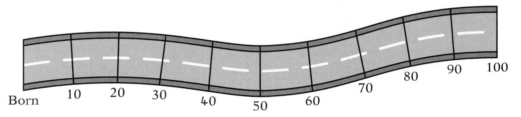

Born   10   20   30   40   50   60   70   80   90   100

a Draw yourself where you are now on the roadway.

b In each box write down what you want to be doing or where you want to be at that age. Here is an example:

I want to retire. I want to have a nice garden and grandchildren.

60   70

c Write a list of any events you know will be certain.

For each statement write down whether it is certain or not certain.

2   You were born.

3   You will go on holiday next year.

4   You will win the lottery.

5   You will eat breakfast tomorrow.

6   Your friend will see you tonight.

7   You will die.

8   You will get married.

9   You will go home after school.

10   You will laugh next week.

TALKING POINT

Are some things impossible?
People thought it was impossible to
go into space, but now explorers
visit space regularly.

Have you seen special effects in
films that are impossible in real
life? How do film makers make
them look possible?

B   For each statement write down whether it is impossible or possible.

1   You will win the lottery.

2   You will travel to the moon.

3   You will never die.

4   Your friend will visit the North Pole this evening.

5   Your arms will grow 20 centimetres overnight.

6   You will go to the cinema next week.

7   You will play a computer game before you are 25.

8   You will receive a text message on your mobile by next Friday.

9   You will wake up with purple hair tomorrow morning.

C   Some things are more likely to happen than others.
Write down which is more likely to happen.

a   Eat toast for breakfast or eat roast beef for breakfast

b   Run 100 metres in 1 minute or run 100 metres in 1 hour

c   Write in blood or write in ink

d   Win the lottery or win at a fair.

REVISION

CHECK IT OUT

1 For each statement write down whether it is certain or not certain.
   a You will go to sleep over the next week.
   b You will make a cake tomorrow.
   c You will have a birthday next year.

2 For each statement write down whether it is impossible or possible.
   a If you plant a stone a rock will grow.
   b If you plant a seed a plant will grow.
   c If you plant a piece of spaghetti a spaghetti tree will grow.

2.23 THE LANGUAGE OF DATA HANDLING

A Sort the words to make a sensible sentence.

1 seven Six smaller is than
2 two than Eight greater is
3 smaller is Twelve than twenty
4 than Eleven greater is four
5 ten smaller Five than is
6 your table results Record in a
7 in Put a tallies chart tally
8 means how Frequency many
9 the order numbers Put in
10 Every title a should graph have

TALKING POINT

When the letters of a word are jumbled up it is called an **anagram**.

Anagrams are used as clues in crosswords.

They are also used in the TV programme *Countdown*.

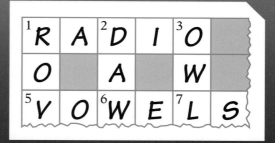

B Solve these anagrams.
Re-arrange the letters to make a word.

1 L L A Y T   T _ _ _ _
2 D R O R E   _ _ _ E _
3 R T C H A   _ H _ _ _
4 E M O T H D   M _ _ _ _ _
5 L I T E T   _ _ _ _ _
6 V E Y S R U   _ _ _ _ _ _
7 T A C R E I N   _ _ R _ _ _ N

8 P O S I M S L E B I   __ <u>M</u> __ __ __ __ __ __ __ <u>E</u>

9 O P P L U R A   <u>P</u> __ __ __ __ __ <u>R</u>

10 U N F E R C Y Q E   __ __ __ <u>Q</u> __ __ __ __ __

W C Draw lines to match the beginning and ending of these words. One has been done for you.

REC	GRAM
TA	QUENCY
TAL	ORD
IMPOSS	ULAR
POP	IBLE
PICTO	TAIN
SUR	LY
FRE	BLE
CER	VEY

3.1 NUMBERS

A **1** Write these numbers in order, smallest first.
    a 420, 130, 260, 390, 580
    b 120, 520, 980, 440, 630
    c 750, 830, 210, 350, 570
    d 625, 925, 125, 725, 425, 525
    e 115, 915, 615, 515, 315, 815
    f 720, 920, 485, 615, 585, 270
    g 480, 215, 365, 575, 295, 330
    h 550, 720, 665, 790, 810, 920
    i 411, 521, 191, 281, 771, 381
    j 518, 239, 782, 894, 117, 358

JUST DO IT!

Draw a grid with 4 squares.

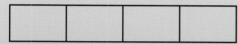

Roll the dice 4 times.
Write each number in the grid.
Try to make the highest or lowest numbers.

2	3	5	7

7	5	3	2

FACT

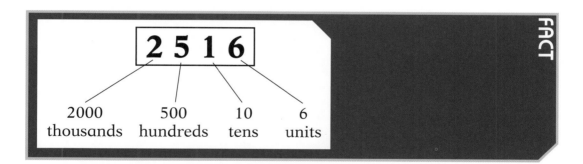

2516

2000	500	10	6
thousands	hundreds	tens	units

2 Write these numbers using digits.
    a three hundred and twenty-five
    b five hundred and seventy-two
    c nine hundred and eighty-one
    d six hundred and sixty-seven
    e two hundred and forty-four
    f three hundred and eighteen
    g seven hundred and thirty-four
    h eight hundred and fifteen
    i one hundred and eleven
    j six hundred and eight

3 Write these numbers in words.

a 257	**d** 229	**g** 614	**j** 507
b 395	**e** 980	**h** 553	**k** 288
c 417	**f** 772	**i** 337	**l** 999

4 Match the words and numbers.

four hundred and two	590
five hundred and ninety	660
four hundred and twelve	519
six hundred and sixty	380
five hundred and nineteen	402
three hundred and eighty	308
three hundred and eight	412

5 These numbers have been written in order.
Which number is out of order?

a 228, 296, 324, 402, 380, 517
b 115, 270, 530, 365, 420, 620
c 250, 450, 510, 620, 850, 710
d 920, 250, 370, 480, 560, 720
e 425, 825, 515, 590, 610, 630
f 150, 160, 210, 170, 180, 190
g 315, 335, 405, 385, 450, 470
h 894, 918, 917, 921, 943, 982

TALKING POINT

As this air balloon rises, how far has it risen after each amount of time
After 1 minute?
After 5 minutes?
After 10 minutes?

B **1** In a quiz, every question is worth 10 points.
Count in 10s to work out each person's score.

QUIZ!

a Ben gets 2 questions correct.
b Anna gets 4 questions correct.
c Joshua gets 1 question correct.
d Paul gets 8 questions correct.
e Dane gets 11 questions correct.
f Claire gets 7 questions correct.
g Hayley gets 6 questions correct.
h Michaela gets 15 questions correct.
i Who gets the highest score?

2   In a second quiz every question is worth 5 points. Count in 5s to work out each person's score.
    a Laura gets 3 questions correct.
    b Kiri gets 5 questions correct.
    c James gets 10 questions correct.
    d Chris gets 8 questions correct.
    e Tara gets 6 questions correct.
    f Hayley gets 11 questions correct.
    g Andy gets 4 questions correct.
    h Dan gets 1 question correct.
    i Jamie gets 7 questions correct.
    j Who gets the highest score?

3   In another quiz every question is worth 100 points. Count in hundreds to work out each person's score.
    a Denise gets 8 questions correct.
    b Holly gets 4 questions correct.
    c Sam gets 3 questions correct.
    d Neil gets 5 questions correct.
    e Toby gets 7 questions correct.
    f Matt gets 6 questions correct.
    g Who gets the highest score?
    h How many more marks does Toby get than Neil?
    i Who scores 200 more than Matt?

> **FACT**
> You can choose any method that works to add, subtract, multiply or divide.

C   In this section you can use a calculator to help you.

1   Find the answer to each addition.

a	270 + 120	**e**	510 + 390	**i**	550 + 360
b	320 + 450	**f**	720 + 140	**j**	120 + 790
c	410 + 460	**g**	390 + 420	**k**	270 + 590
d	380 + 220	**h**	630 + 190	**l**	330 + 680

2   Find the answer to each addition.

a	215 + 325	**e**	370 + 495	**i**	595 + 340
b	425 + 465	**f**	295 + 605	**j**	885 + 105
c	585 + 205	**g**	275 + 715		
d	195 + 110	**h**	465 + 335		

3 Find the missing number in each calculation.

a 250 + ☐ = 1000   f ☐ + 360 = 1000
b 320 + ☐ = 1000   g ☐ + 290 = 1000
c 180 + ☐ = 1000   h ☐ + 100 = 1000
d 260 + ☐ = 1000   i ☐ + 990 = 1000
e 920 + ☐ = 1000   j ☐ + 590 = 1000

4 Find the missing number in each calculation.

a 275 + ☐ = 1000   f ☐ + 105 = 1000
b 125 + ☐ = 1000   g ☐ + 895 = 1000
c 655 + ☐ = 1000   h ☐ + 715 = 1000
d 375 + ☐ = 1000   i ☐ + 865 = 1000
e 495 + ☐ = 1000   j ☐ + 195 = 1000

5 Find the missing number in each calculation.

a 200 + ☐ = 300 + 700
b 500 + ☐ = 600 + 400
c ☐ + 700 = 400 + 600
d 250 + ☐ = 350 + 650
e 150 + 850 = ☐ + 800
f 350 + 650 = 150 + ☐
g 450 + 550 = ☐ + 650

6 Find the missing numbers in this diagram.

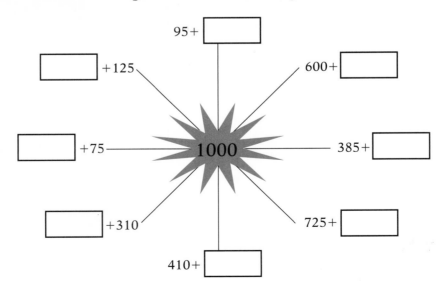

REVISION

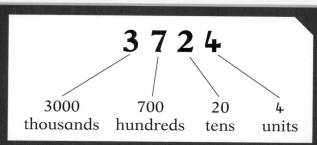

3 7 2 4

3000 thousands

700 hundreds

20 tens

4 units

You can choose any method that works to add, subtract, multiply or divide.

FACT

LEARNING TIPS

Clap as you count up in 10s to 1000. Clapping helps you remember more easily

Count in 5s to 200. Do it against the clock and try to improve your time

Say a number to a friend. They have to give the number that makes it up to 1000. Use a calculator to check their answer

CHECK IT OUT

1 Write these numbers in order, smallest first.
   320, 150, 270, 580, 490

2 Write this number using digits.
   two hundred and fifty-three

3 Write 429 in words.

4 Which number is out of order? 160, 290, 580, 320, 385

5 Count in 10s seven times. Write down the answer.

6 Count in 5s six times. Write down the answer.

7 Count in 100s four times. Write down the answer.

8 Find the missing number in each calculation.
   a 275 + 420 = ☐   **d** ☐ + 195 = 1000
   b 610 + 175 = ☐   **e** ☐ + 495 = 260 + 740
   c 370 + ☐ = 1000

ANSWERS

1 150, 270, 320, 490, 580   **2** 253   **3** four hundred and twenty-nine   **4** 580   **5** 70   **6** 30   **7** 400   **8a** 695   **b** 785   **c** 630   **d** 805   **e** 505

101

3.2   FRACTIONS

TALKING POINT

'A fraction of the time'
'Quarter-back'
'Half a chance'
'Quarter past four'
'A fraction of the cost'
All these expressions have fractions in them.
Discuss what each one means.
Do you know any other expressions which have fractions in them?
What do you think **fraction** means?

W A   **1**   Shade one half ($\frac{1}{2}$) of each shape.

a   **c**   **e**

b 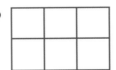   **d**   **f**

W   **2**   Shade one quarter ($\frac{1}{4}$) of each shape.

a   **c**   **e**

b    **d**   **f**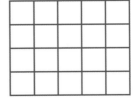

W **3** Shade three quarters ($\frac{3}{4}$) of each shape.

a

c

e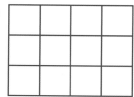

b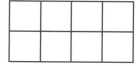

d

f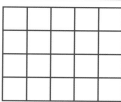

W **4** Shade one tenth ($\frac{1}{10}$) of each shape.

a

c

b

d

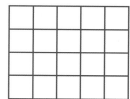

W **5** Shade the given fraction of each shape.

a $\frac{3}{10}$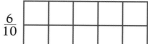

e $\frac{6}{10}$

b $\frac{7}{10}$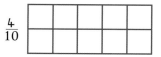

f $\frac{6}{10}$

c $\frac{4}{10}$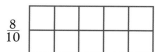

g $\frac{9}{10}$

d $\frac{8}{10}$

h $\frac{2}{10}$

Finding **fractions** means splitting shapes or numbers into **equal amounts**.

FACT

B **1** Find half ($\frac{1}{2}$) of each amount.

a	£10	**e**	£40	**i**	2 mm	**m**	£3
b	£8	**f**	£50	**j**	10 mm	**n**	£7
c	£12	**g**	£18	**k**	18 mm	**o**	£11
d	£20	**h**	£28	**l**	30 mm	**p**	£15

2 Find a quarter ($\frac{1}{4}$) of each amount.

a	£4	**c**	£20	**e**	12 mm	**g**	£10
b	£8	**d**	£40	**f**	24 mm	**h**	£18

3 Find three quarters ($\frac{3}{4}$) of each amount.

a	£4	**c**	£24	**e**	16 mm	**g**	£10
b	£12	**d**	£44	**f**	40 mm	**h**	£6

4 Find one tenth ($\frac{1}{10}$) of each amount.

a	£10	**c**	£40	**e**	30 mm	**g**	70 mm
b	£20	**d**	£80	**f**	60 mm	**h**	50 mm

5 Find the fraction of each amount.

a $\frac{3}{10}$ of £20

b $\frac{5}{10}$ of £30

c $\frac{7}{10}$ of £10

d $\frac{4}{10}$ of £30

e $\frac{9}{10}$ of 60 mm

f $\frac{2}{10}$ of 90 mm

g $\frac{6}{10}$ of £40

h $\frac{8}{10}$ of £70

TALKING POINT

1 Which would you rather have, $\frac{3}{4}$ of £100 or $\frac{6}{10}$ of £120?
$\frac{3}{4}$ of £100 = £75 $\frac{6}{10}$ of £120 = £72

2 How much money would you win if you won three quarters of a million pounds? Would it be enough to buy a yacht that costs £800 000?

3 If you have £60 but your friend has 'half as much again', how much has your friend got?

C   1   Which amount is larger?

    a $\frac{1}{2}$ of 26 or $\frac{3}{4}$ of 12?

    b $\frac{1}{4}$ of 80 or $\frac{3}{4}$ of 28?

    c $\frac{3}{4}$ of 24 or $\frac{1}{2}$ of 30?

    d $\frac{1}{2}$ of 40 or $\frac{3}{4}$ of 60?

    e $\frac{3}{4}$ of 16 or $\frac{1}{4}$ of 40?

    f $\frac{3}{10}$ of 30 or $\frac{1}{4}$ of 40?

    g $\frac{3}{4}$ of 16 or $\frac{7}{10}$ of 20?

    h $\frac{1}{2}$ of 70 or $\frac{9}{10}$ of 40?

    i $\frac{4}{10}$ of 30 or $\frac{1}{2}$ of 28?

    j $\frac{3}{4}$ of 60 or $\frac{6}{10}$ of 70?

  2   Which amount is smaller?

    a $\frac{1}{2}$ of £24 or $\frac{1}{4}$ of £50?

    b $\frac{3}{4}$ of £60 or $\frac{1}{2}$ of £80?

    c $\frac{3}{4}$ of £40 or $\frac{1}{4}$ of £100?

    d $\frac{3}{10}$ of £60 or $\frac{1}{2}$ of £50?

    e $\frac{7}{10}$ of £30 or $\frac{3}{4}$ of £40?

    f $\frac{3}{4}$ of £20 or $\frac{2}{10}$ of £80?

JUST DO IT!

This is a fraction chain:

5 is $\frac{1}{2}$ of 10 which is $\frac{1}{2}$ of 20 which is half of 40 which is half of 80 which is …

1   How far can you go with this fraction chain?

2   Make some fraction chains of your own with different starting numbers.

3   Make some fraction chains with different fractions. For example: 3 is $\frac{1}{10}$ of 30 which is $\frac{1}{10}$ of 300 …

4   Make a poster of your work for display.

REVISION

Finding **fractions** means splitting shapes or numbers into **equal amounts**.

LEARNING TIPS

Cut up cakes or chocolate into equal amounts to help you get the idea of fractions ... then eat them!

Practise splitting numbers into 2, 4 or 10 in your head. This will help you find fractions more quickly

Look for fractions in everyday life. Work out the answers in your head

CHECK IT OUT

1   How much of each shape is shaded?

a   **b** 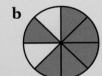   **c** 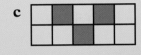   **d**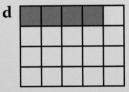

2   Find the fraction of each amount.
   a $\frac{1}{2}$ of £24   **b** $\frac{3}{4}$ of £16   **c** $\frac{1}{4}$ of 32 mm   **d** $\frac{6}{10}$ of 80 mm

3   Which amount is larger?
   a $\frac{3}{4}$ of 24 or $\frac{1}{2}$ of 30?
   b $\frac{6}{10}$ of 20 or $\frac{3}{10}$ or 30?

4   Which amount is smaller?
   a $\frac{1}{2}$ of £24 or $\frac{3}{10}$ of £30?
   b $\frac{7}{10}$ or £70 or $\frac{6}{10}$ of £80?

3.3 NEGATIVE NUMBERS

> A **negative number** is a number less than 0.
> A **positive number** is a number greater than 0.
> 0 is neither negative nor positive.

JUST DO IT!

Make a number line.
Cut paper into strips and join them together.
Draw a line along the middle of the paper.
Mark every 2 cm along the line.
Make the middle mark larger than the others.
This is '0'.

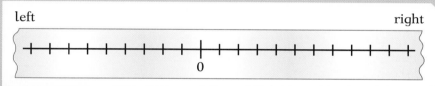

Start at 0. Label the numbers going *right* from 1 to the end.

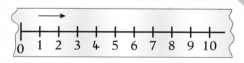

Start at 0. Label the numbers going left from −1 to the end.

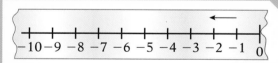

You can use this number line to help you learn about negative numbers.

A   **1**   Write down the missing number from each section of number line.

a
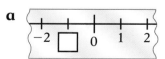

b
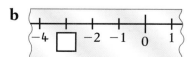

c
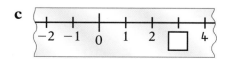

d
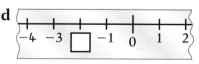

e
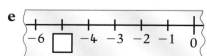

f
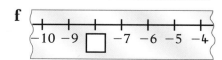

2 Write down the 2 missing numbers from each section of number line.

a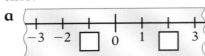

d

b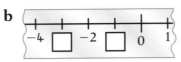

e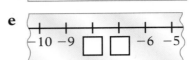

c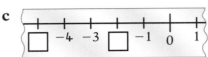

f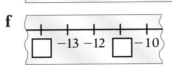

Adding negative numbers is the same as **subtracting positive numbers.**

FACT

JUST DO IT!

Play this game with a friend.
Use a calculator.

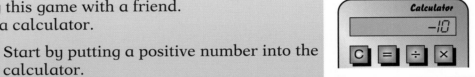

1 Start by putting a positive number into the calculator.

2 Add a negative number.

3 Guess whether the answer will be positive or negative. You score 1 point every time you are correct.

You can make the game more difficult by trying to guess or work out the correct answer.

B **1** Which is the smallest number in each pair?

a 4, 6	**d** 0, −2	**g** 9, −2
b −2, 3	**e** −5, −2	**h** −15, −14
c 5, −1	**f** −10, −12	**i** 5, −20

2 Write these numbers in order, smallest first.

a 0, 2, −1, 4	**d** −4, −2, −6, −1
b −3, −1, 1, 0	**e** −10, −7, −12, −4
c −5, 5, 1, 2	**f** 20, −15, 18, −3, 0

3 Write down which two numbers would be next to each other on a number line.

a −4, 3, 0, 2	**d** 9, −2, −3, 8
b 5, −2, 1, −3	**e** −20, −4, −18, −5
c −10, −3, −4, −7	**f** 6, 0, −8, −10, 11, −11

JUST DO IT!

Use a thermometer to take your temperature.
Find out the different ways of measuring temperature.
Use the Internet to find temperatures around the world. Find out
which countries have positive temperatures and which have negative
temperatures.
Put your results in a table.

C These thermometers measure temperature in °C (degrees Celsius).
Write down the temperature on each thermometer. Write down if the
answer is positive or negative.

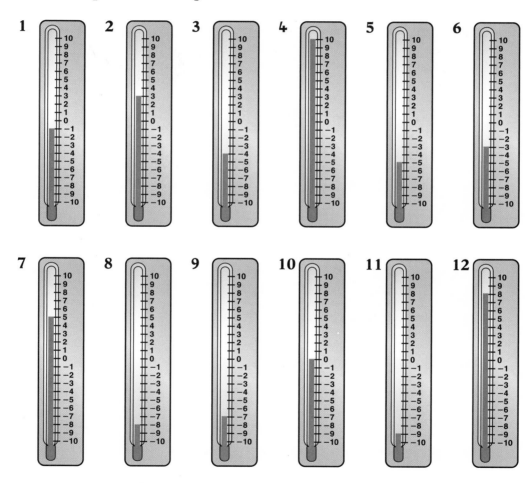

REVISION

A **negative number** is a number less than 0.

A **positive number** is a number greater than 0.

0 is neither negative nor positive.

Adding negative numbers is the same as **subtracting positive numbers**.

LEARNING TIPS

Remember that negative numbers seem to go backwards as you write them from right to left

If you compare two negative numbers the lowest digit is the highest number

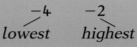

lowest   *highest*

Look for the temperature on the freezers in the supermarket

CHECK IT OUT

1 Write down the missing numbers from each number line.

a 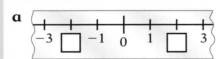   **b**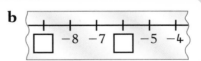

2 Which number is smaller, −8 or −6?

3 Write these numbers in order, smallest first.
−4, −9, 6, −8, 3

4 Write down the temperature shown on this thermometer.

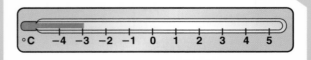

ANSWERS

1a −2, 2   **b** −6, −9   **2** −8   **3** −9, −8, −4, 3, 6   **4** −3°C

3.4 SEQUENCES

A **sequence** is a list of numbers that follow a pattern.

A

1 All these sequences go up or down in 2s.
Write down the next 2 numbers in each sequence.

a 0, 2, 4, 6, ...
b 3, 5, 7, 9, ...
c 15, 13, 11, 9, ...
d 10, 8, 6, 4, ...
e 7, 9, 11, 13, ...

f 10, 12, 14, 16, ...
g 20, 18, 16, 14, ...
h 22, 24, 26, 28, ...
i 14, 12, 10, 8, ...
j 6, 8, 10, 12, ...

2 Find the missing numbers in each sequence.

a 2, ☐, 6, 8, ☐, 12, 14
b 5, 7, 9, ☐, 13, ☐, 17
c 1, 3, ☐, ☐, 9, 11, ☐
d 20, 18, ☐, 14, 12, ☐, 8
e 17, 15, 13, ☐, ☐, 7, 5
f 8, ☐, ☐, ☐, 16, 18, 20
g ☐, ☐, 13, 15, 17, ☐, 21
h ☐, ☐, 18, 20, ☐, 24, ☐

3 All these sequences go up or down in 3s.
Write down the next 2 numbers in each sequence.

a 0, 3, 6, 9, ...
b 1, 4, 7, 10, ...
c 3, 6, 9, 12, ...
d 5, 8, 11, 14, ...
e 18, 15, 12, 9, ...

f 24, 21, 18, 15, ...
g 16, 13, 10, 7, ...
h 9, 12, 15, 18, ...
i 7, 10, 13, 16, ...
j 12, 15, 18, 21, ...

4 Find the missing numbers in each sequence.

a 1, ☐, 7, ☐, 13, 16, 19
b 9, ☐, 15, 18, ☐, 24, 27
c 30, 27, ☐, 21, 18, ☐, 12
d 7, 10, ☐, ☐, ☐, 22, 25
e 22, 19, ☐, 13, ☐, ☐, 4
f ☐, 6, ☐, 12, ☐, 18, 21
g 2, ☐, ☐, ☐, 14, ☐, 20
h 24, ☐, 18, ☐, ☐, ☐, 6

5 All these sequences go up or down in 4s.
Write down the next 2 numbers in each sequence.

  a 0, 4, 8, 12, ...   **f** 10, 14, 18, 22, ...
  b 2, 6, 10, 14, ...   **g** 5, 9, 13, 17, ...
  c 1, 5, 9, 13, ...   **h** 3, 7, 11, 15, ...
  d 30, 26, 22, 18, ...   **i** 29, 25, 21, 17, ...
  e 28, 24, 20, 16, ...   **j** 8, 12, 16, 20, ...

6 Find the missing numbers in each sequence.

  a 3, 7, ☐, 15, ☐, 23
  b ☐, 4, 8, 12, ☐, 20
  c 30, ☐, 22, ☐, 14, 10
  d 27, 23, ☐, 15, ☐, 7
  e ☐, 24, 20, ☐, 12, 8
  f 8, 12, 16, ☐, ☐, 28
  g 5, 9, ☐, ☐, 21, 25
  h 15, 19, 23, ☐, ☐, 35

> Each number in a **sequence** is called a term.
>
> **FACT**

JUST DO IT!

Write down 15 terms in the sequence that goes up in 2s and starts with 3.
Write down 15 terms in the sequence that goes up in 3s and starts with 3.

How many numbers appear in both sequences?
Which numbers are they?

B **1** All these sequences go up or down in 5s.
Write down the next 2 numbers in each sequence.

  a 0, 5, 10, 15, ...   **f** 4, 9, 14, 19, ...
  b 2, 7, 12, 17, ...   **g** 8, 13, 18, 23, ...
  c 30, 25, 20, 15, ...   **h** 34, 29, 24, 19, ...
  d 50, 45, 40, 35, ...   **i** 28, 23, 18, 13, ...
  e 3, 8, 13, 18, ...   **j** 6, 11, 16, 21, ...

2 Find the missing numbers in each sequence.
    a 3, ☐, 13, 18, ☐, 28
    b 7, 12, ☐, ☐, 27, 32
    c ☐, 6, 11, 16, ☐, 26
    d 40, ☐, ☐, 35, 30, 25
    e 30, 25, ☐, 15, 10, ☐
    f 8, ☐, ☐, 23, 28, 33, 38
    g 12, 17, 22, ☐, 32, ☐, 42
    h 9, 14, 19, ☐, ☐, 34, 39

3 All these sequences go up or down in 10s.
    Write down the next 2 numbers in each sequence.

a 4, 14, 24, 34, …	**f** 72, 62, 52, 42, …
b 6, 16, 26, 36, …	**g** 13, 23, 33, 43, …
c 30, 40, 50, 60, …	**h** 29, 39, 49, 59, …
d 27, 37, 47, 57, …	**i** 83, 73, 63, 53, …
e 90, 80, 70, 60, …	**j** 19, 29, 39, 49, …

4 Find the missing numbers in each sequence.

a 12, ☐, 32, 42, ☐, 62	**e** 100, ☐, 80, 70, ☐, ☐
b 7, 17, ☐, ☐, 47, 57	**f** 82, 72, ☐, ☐, 42, 32
c 13, 23, 33, ☐, 53, ☐	**g** ☐, 20, 30, ☐, 50, ☐
d 31, ☐, 51, 61, ☐, 81	**h** 19, ☐, ☐, 49, 59, 69

JUST DO IT!

Make up some sequence sentences like this one.

sequence: 2   3   4   5
sentence: Is the ball round?

The sequence number and the number of letters in the word are the same.

C **1** Write down the pattern for each sequence.

a 9, 12, 15, 18, 21	**f** 40, 35, 30, 25, 20
b 5, 10, 15, 20, 25	**g** 31, 29, 27, 25, 23
c 3, 7, 11, 15, 19	**h** 6, 11, 16, 21, 26
d 9, 19, 29, 39, 49	**i** 50, 46, 42, 38, 34
e 18, 16, 14, 12, 10	**j** 13, 16, 19, 22, 25

2 Find the missing numbers in each sequence.

   a 82, 72, ☐, ☐, 42, 32, ☐

   b 100, 96, ☐, 88, 84, ☐, 76

   c ☐, 10, 15, ☐, ☐, 30, ☐

   d 17, ☐, 27, 32, ☐, ☐, 47

   e 46, 43, ☐, 37, ☐, ☐, ☐

   f 89, ☐, 93, ☐, ☐, 99, ☐

3 Each sequence has been split in two. Match the beginnings and endings to make complete sequences.

2	4	6
5	10	15
3	7	10
0	4	8
3	6	9
4	9	14
1	3	5

20	25	30
12	16	20
12	15	18
8	10	12
19	24	29
7	9	11
13	16	19

REVISION

A **sequence** is a list of numbers that follow a pattern.
Each number in a sequence is called a **term**.

LEARNING TIPS

Learning your multiplication tables will help you understand sequences

Look for patterns in the numbers. Do they end in the same digit?

Sequences going up in 4s go up twice as quickly as sequences going up in 2s

CHECK IT OUT

1 Write down the next 2 numbers in each sequence.
   a 3, 5, 7, 9, …
   b 8, 11, 14, 17, …
   c 25, 29, 33, 37, …
   d 3, 8, 13, 18, …
   e 97, 87, 77, 67, …

2 Find the missing numbers in each sequence.
   a 8, ☐, 12, ☐, 16
   b 9, ☐, ☐, 18, 21
   c ☐, 9, 13, ☐, 21
   d 87, ☐, 67, ☐, 47
   e 13, 23, ☐, 43, ☐

3 Write down the pattern for each sequence.
   a 11, 15, 19, 23, 27
   b 60, 58, 56, 54, 52

3a goes up in 4s **b** goes down in 2s
2a 10, 14 **b** 12, 15 **c** 5, 17 **d** 77, 57 **e** 33, 53
1a 11, 13 **b** 20, 23 **c** 41, 45 **d** 23, 28 **e** 57, 47

ANSWERS

3.5   DIVISION

JUST DO IT!

You can use a calculator for this activity.
Start with 40 on the calculator.
Subtract 8.
Keep subtracting 8 until the display is '0'.
Write down the number of times you subtracted 8.

$$40 - 8 - 8 - 8 - 8 - 8 = 0$$

This tells you that $40 \div 8 = 5$.

Now do the same for these numbers.
Copy the table and fill it in.

input	subtract	number of times	sum
40	8	5	$40 \div 8 = 5$
20	4		
16	2		
30	5		
24	6		

You can **divide** using repeated **subtraction**.

FACT

A   **1**   Use repeated subtraction to work out these divisions.

    a $24 \div 4$ **e** $15 \div 5$ **i** $36 \div 3$

    b $12 \div 3$ **f** $70 \div 10$ **j** $32 \div 4$

    c $18 \div 3$ **g** $28 \div 4$ **k** $40 \div 5$

    d $90 \div 10$ **h** $20 \div 2$ **l** $25 \div 5$

2   All these divisions have a remainder.
Use repeated subtraction to work out these divisions.

Example: $20 \div 3 = 20 - 3 - 3 - 3 - 3 - 3 - 3$
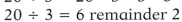
                $20 \div 3 = 6$ remainder 2

    a $14 \div 3$ **e** $23 \div 5$ **i** $36 \div 5$

    b $22 \div 4$ **f** $17 \div 2$ **j** $27 \div 5$

    c $27 \div 10$ **g** $42 \div 10$ **k** $29 \div 3$

    d $18 \div 4$ **h** $51 \div 10$ **l** $31 \div 4$

3 Use repeated subtraction for these divisions. Some have
remainders and some do not.

a	$20 \div 4$	**e**	$40 \div 10$	**i**	$72 \div 10$
b	$13 \div 3$	**f**	$16 \div 4$	**j**	$85 \div 10$
c	$18 \div 5$	**g**	$26 \div 2$	**k**	$38 \div 4$
d	$24 \div 5$	**h**	$38 \div 5$	**l**	$19 \div 10$

4 **a** Mike and his friends were sharing their money equally. Mike
     had £8 and 3 friends. How much did they have each?

   b Jack and his 3 friends shared £22.
       How much did they have each?

   c Polly and her 3 friends shared £28.
       How much did they have each?

   d Charlene and her 4 friends shared £30.
       How much did they have each?

   e Abi and her 9 friends shared £40.
       How much did they have each?

   f Dave and his 4 friends shared £28.
       How much did they have each?

   g Kieren and his 9 friends shared £25.
       How much did they have each?

   h Terri and her 3 friends shared £17.
       How much did they have each?

   i Claire and her 4 friends shared £51.
       How much did they have each?

   j Nikki and her 2 friends shared £29.
       How much did they have each?

JUST DO IT!

It is useful to divide your time sensibly. You can get your work done
and have time to relax.
Use the Time Planning Worksheet.

1 Fill in all the time you are at school.

2 Fill in all the clubs and activities that you do every week.

3 Fill in how many hours of homework you have to do.

4 Keep filling in the Time Planner, then see how much free time
you have left.

$$\overset{\displaystyle 3\ 9}{2\overline{)7^18}}$$ This is a method for **short division**.

It means $78 \div 2 = 39$

FACT

B **1** Find the solutions to these calculations.

a $2\overline{)42}$ g $2\overline{)88}$ m $2\overline{)92}$

b $3\overline{)36}$ h $5\overline{)95}$ n $2\overline{)58}$

c $5\overline{)45}$ i $5\overline{)25}$ o $3\overline{)57}$

d $4\overline{)84}$ j $2\overline{)26}$ p $4\overline{)68}$

e $3\overline{)72}$ k $3\overline{)42}$ q $5\overline{)80}$

f $5\overline{)65}$ l $4\overline{)60}$ r $3\overline{)48}$

2 Find the solutions to these calculations.

a $28 \div 2$ f $48 \div 4$ k $78 \div 2$

b $39 \div 3$ g $52 \div 4$ l $96 \div 4$

c $50 \div 5$ h $40 \div 10$ m $96 \div 3$

d $90 \div 2$ i $40 \div 5$ n $96 \div 2$

e $38 \div 2$ j $84 \div 4$ o $90 \div 5$

JUST DO IT!

Copy the grid onto squared paper and solve the divisions to fill it in.

Division 2

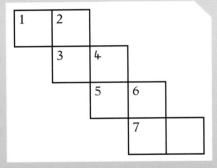

Across

1 $22 \div 2$

3 $42 \div 2$

5 $62 \div 2$

7 $48 \div 2$

Down

2 $24 \div 2$

4 $26 \div 2$

6 $28 \div 2$

Make up your own *Division 2* puzzle using this grid:

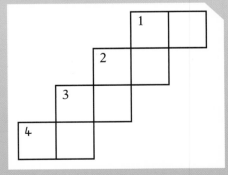

Across

1

2

3

4

Down

1

2

3

Some division answers will have a remainder.

C **1** Fariq and his friends each get a different package for free access to the Internet.
They want to spread their Internet time equally over the week.
For each person work out how long they will have each night.

a Tariq – 14 hours per week
b Jason – 27 hours per week
c Sufyana – 35 hours per week
d Min – 10 hours per week
e Sally – 15 hours per week
f John – 20 hours per week
g Thomas – 24 hours per week
h Nikki – 18 hours per week

2 A supermarket manager is planning the new car parks for his superstore.
Each bay is 2 metres wide.
Work out how many cars will fit into each car park.

a Car Park A

10 metres

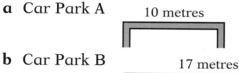

b Car Park B

17 metres

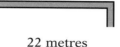

c Car Park C

22 metres

d Car Park D

30 metres

e Car Park E

90 metres

f Car Park F

47 metres

The lorry parks need bays that measure 3 metres across.
Work out how many lorries will fit into each lorry park.

g Lorry Park G

12 metres

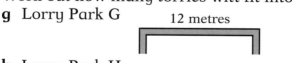

h Lorry Park H

18 metres

i Lorry Park I

22 metres

j Lorry Park J

17 metres

k Lorry Park K

32 metres

FACT

Whole numbers that divide by 10 without a remainder always end with 0.

D

1 Which of these numbers divide by 10 without a remainder?

a 30	**d** 90	**g** 10	**j** 20
b 42	**e** 72	**h** 18	**k** 60
c 27	**f** 80	**i** 21	**l** 100

2 Divide each number by 10 *and* give the remainder.

a 36	**c** 42	**e** 31	**g** 56
b 20	**d** 89	**f** 44	**h** 50

3 Write down the number for each description
  a When you divide by 10 the answer is 3 remainder 4
  b When you divide by 10 the answer is 7 remainder 2
  c When you divide by 10 the answer is 8 with no remainder
  d When you divide by 10 the answer is 6 remainder 1
  e When you divide by 10 the answer is 2 remainder 9
  f When you divide by 10 the answer is 4 remainder 5

REVISION

FACT

You can **divide** using repeated **subtraction**:

$$2\overline{)7^18}$$ means $78 \div 2 = 39$ (quotient $3\,9$)

This is a method for **short division**.

LEARNING TIPS

Sort piles of buttons into those with 2 holes and those with 4 holes, then divide each group into 5 equal piles

Always check for remainders when you divide

CHECK IT OUT

1   Use repeated subtraction to work out the solutions to these calculations.

    a $30 \div 2$ **c** $28 \div 4$ **e** $43 \div 5$

    b $18 \div 3$ **d** $66 \div 4$ **f** $38 \div 10$

2   **a** Share £28 between 4 people.
    b Share £28 between 5 people.

3   Work out the solutions to these calculations.

    a $2\overline{)23}$ **b** $4\overline{)44}$ **c** $5\overline{)65}$

4   Maggie has 22 hours of Internet time to use over 1 week. Allocate the time equally over the week.

5   Which of these numbers divide by 10 without a remainder?

    40   20   17   70   60   26

3.6 MULTIPLICATION

> When you multiply a whole number by 10 it is the same as putting a zero on the end.

A

1 Find the answer to each calculation.

a 4×10	**e** 5×10	**i** 16×10
b 6×10	**f** 7×10	**j** 22×10
c 3×10	**g** 10×10	**k** 25×10
d 1×10	**h** 12×10	**l** 31×10

2 Find the missing number in each calculation.

a $16 \times \boxed{} = 160$

b $\boxed{} \times 10 = 80$

c $11 \times 10 = \boxed{}$

d $28 \times \boxed{} = 280$

e $\boxed{} \times 10 = 170$

f $\boxed{} \times 10 = 380$

g $\boxed{} \times 10 = 400$

h $33 \times 10 = \boxed{}$

i $57 \times 10 = \boxed{}$

j $39 \times \boxed{} = 390$

3 **a** Paulo buys 10 CDs. Each one costs £11. How much does he spend?

b Denise buys 10 magazines. How much does she spend if each one costs £3?

c Brian buys 10 take-away meals for his friends. Each one costs £4. How much does he spend altogether?

d Lucy buys 10 pens for her exams. Each one costs 7 p. How much change does she get from £1?

e 10 copies of a book are lined up on a shelf which measures 40 cm. Each book is 3 cm wide. How much spare room is there on the shelf?

4 Fill in the missing symbol or number in each calculation.

a $4 \boxed{} 10 = 40$

b $70 \boxed{} 10 = 7$

c $\boxed{} \times 10 = 50$

d $13 \boxed{} 10 = 130$

e $180 \boxed{} 10 = 18$

f $270 \div \boxed{} = 27$

g $\boxed{} \div 10 = 14$

h $\boxed{} \times 10 = 520$

i $370 \boxed{} 10 = 37$

j $98 \times 10 = \boxed{}$

W ## JUST DO IT!

You need a Multiplication Worksheet and a stopwatch or clock with a second hand. Complete the first multiplication square on the worksheet. Write down how long this took.
Either fill in all six squares on the sheet, trying to beat your time
or fill in one square a day and try to beat your time.

Target times:
1 minute – You need to practise!
45 seconds – A good speed
30 seconds – This is good
15 seconds – Extremely speedy!!

×	1	2	3	4	5
1					
2					
3					
4					
5					

B **1** Find the answer to each of these calculations.

a 4×3 **d** 8×10 **g** 5×5 **j** 4×4
b 3×5 **e** 2×5 **h** 5×3 **k** 5×4
c 2×4 **f** 4×5 **i** 2×2 **l** 3×3

2 Fill in the missing numbers in each calculation.

a $\square \times 5 = 10$ **e** $\square \times 2 = 8$ **i** $5 \times \square = 25$
b $3 \times \square = 12$ **f** $2 \times 2 = \square$ **j** $\square \times 3 = 9$
c $5 \times \square = 15$ **g** $\square \times 5 = 15$ **k** $\square \times 4 = 16$
d $4 \times 4 = \square$ **h** $2 \times \square = 10$ **l** $4 \times \square = 20$

In the school tuck shop you can buy these:

chews   gumballs   flippers   toffee drops
2 p   3 p   4 p   5 p

3 Find how much each of these will cost.

a 10 chews   **g** 4 toffee drops
b 4 gumballs   **h** 5 chews
c 4 flippers   **i** 4 chews and 1 gumball
d 3 toffee drops   **j** 10 gumballs and 2 toffee drops
e 3 flippers   **k** 3 flippers and 5 gumballs
f 5 gumballs   **l** 4 gumballs and 4 toffee drops

4 Work out whether each statement is true or false.
  a 4 chews and 2 flippers cost 12p.
  b 3 gumballs and 8 toffee drops cost less than 50p.
  c 8 flippers costs the same as 4 chews.
  d 2 toffee drops and 2 chews cost more than 2 gumballs and 2 flippers.
  e 10 of everything costs exactly £1.

5 Write down an example of what you could buy for each of these amounts.
  a 12p   **b** 19p   **c** 22p   **d** 30p

6 Work out the change from £1 for each of these purchases.
  a 10 flippers
  b 10 gumballs
  c 5 chews and 4 toffee drops
  d 10 toffee drops and 4 gumballs
  e 10 flippers, 5 chews and 5 gumballs

JUST DO IT!

1 Use a blank 5 by 5 Multiplication Square.
Fill in the answers. Then:
  a colour the numbers that appear once in yellow
  b colour the numbers that appear twice in green
  c colour the numbers that appear three times in red.

×	1	2	3	4	5
1	1	2	3	4	5
2	2	4	6	8	10
3	3	6	9	12	15
4	4	8	12	16	20
5	5	10	15	20	25

2 Write the numbers 1 to 25. Put a circle around the numbers that appear in the 5 by 5 Multiplication Square. Use the same colours as before.

① 2 3 4 5 6 7 8 ⑨ 10 11 12 13 14
15 ⑯ 17 18 19 20 21 22 23 24 ㉕

3 Make a list of the numbers without circles around them.

C Some calculations give the same answer as others:
$$4 \times 5 = 20 \qquad 2 \times 10 = 20$$
$$4 \times 5 = 2 \times 10$$

1 Match the calculations that have the same answer.

4×5	1×4
3×5	2×6
2×2	2×4
4×2	10×2
3×4	5×3

2 For each question write down which calculation gives the largest answer.

a 4×3 or 2×5 **c** 4×4 or 5×3 **e** 5×4 or 10×3

b 4×2 or 3×3 **d** 2×3 or 1×4 **f** 4×2 or 3×3

3 a *2 times table*   *4 times table*

$1 \times 2 = 2$ $1 \times 4 = 4$

$2 \times 2 = 4$ $2 \times 4 = 8$

$3 \times 2 = 6$ $3 \times 4 = 12$

$4 \times 2 = 8$ $4 \times 4 = 16$

$5 \times 2 = 10$ $5 \times 4 = 20$

Write down the connection between the answers to the 2 times table and those for the 4 times table.

b *5 times table*   *10 times table*

$1 \times 5 = 5$ $1 \times 10 = 10$

$2 \times 5 = 10$ $2 \times 10 = 20$

$3 \times 5 = 15$ $3 \times 10 = 30$

$4 \times 5 = 20$ $4 \times 10 = 40$

$5 \times 5 = 25$ $5 \times 10 = 50$

Write down the connection between the answers to the 5 times table and those for the 10 times table.

REVISION

FACT

When you multiply a whole number by 10 it is the same as putting a 0 on the end.

LEARNING TIPS

Chant your multiplication tables in full, not just the answer …
'one times two is two'
'two times two is four' etc.

Look for patterns in the multiplication tables

CHECK IT OUT

1 Find the answers to these calculations.
   a 5×10 b 10×28

2 Fill in the missing number or symbol.
   a $60 \ \square \ 10 = 6$ b $14 \ \square \ 10 = 140$ c $\square \times 10 = 270$

3 Write down the answers to these.
   a 4×5 b 3×4 c 10×2

4 a How much do 5 pencils at 3p cost altogether?
   b If Jason buys 10 magazines at £4 how much does he pay?
   c Susie buys 4 sweets costing 2p, 5 sweets costing 4p and 3 sweets costing 5p. How much change does she get from £1?

ANSWERS

1a 50 b 280   2a ÷ b × c 27   3a 20 b 12 c 20
4a 15p b £40 c 57p

3.7   MORE MONEY

JUST DO IT!

The money used in different countries is called currency.
Currencies have a name and a symbol.
In the United Kingdom the currency is pounds.

country	currency	symbol
UK	pounds	£
United States	dollars	$

Find the currency for some other countries and put your results in a
table like the one above.

A   **1**   Write down how much money is in each picture.

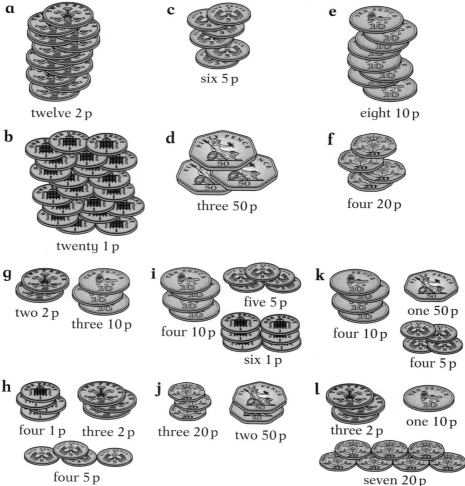

a

twelve 2 p

c

six 5 p

e

eight 10 p

b

twenty 1 p

d

three 50 p

f

four 20 p

g

two 2 p   three 10 p

i

five 5 p

four 10 p   six 1 p

k

four 10 p   one 50 p

four 5 p

h

four 1 p   three 2 p

four 5 p

j

three 20 p   two 50 p

l

three 2 p   one 10 p

seven 20 p

2   Match the amounts of money that have the same value.

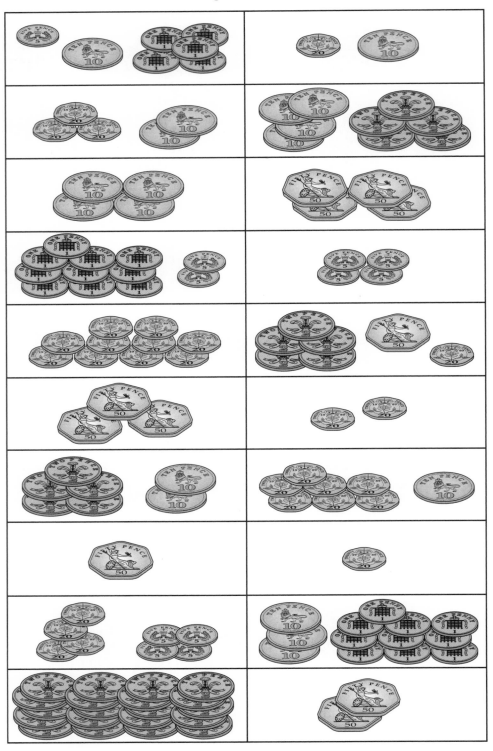

3 Find out how much money is in each pile. Write the amounts in order, smallest first.

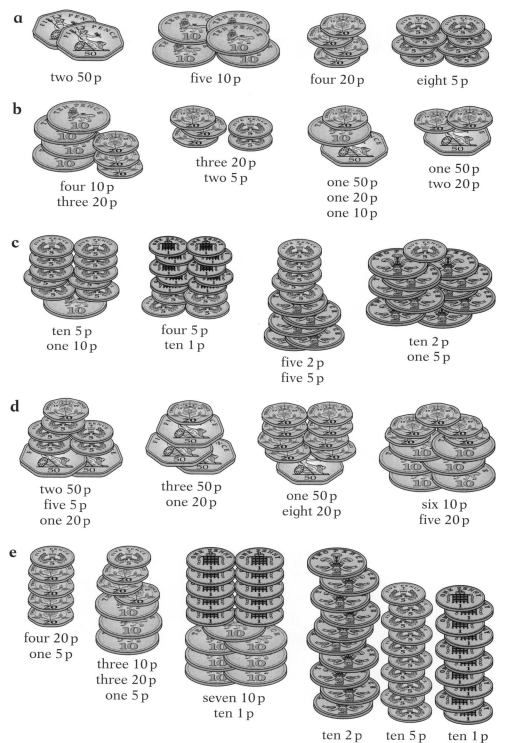

a

two 50 p

five 10 p

four 20 p

eight 5 p

b

four 10 p
three 20 p

three 20 p
two 5 p

one 50 p
one 20 p
one 10 p

one 50 p
two 20 p

c

ten 5 p
one 10 p

four 5 p
ten 1 p

five 2 p
five 5 p

ten 2 p
one 5 p

d

two 50 p
five 5 p
one 20 p

three 50 p
one 20 p

one 50 p
eight 20 p

six 10 p
five 20 p

e

four 20 p
one 5 p

three 10 p
three 20 p
one 5 p

seven 10 p
ten 1 p

ten 2 p   ten 5 p   ten 1 p

JUST DO IT!

Find all the different ways of making 50p using 5p, 10p and 20p coins.

6 ways – OK
8 ways – Good
10 ways – Very good
12 ways – Fantastic!

B

   1p   2p   5p   10p   20p   50p   £1

1 Choose the coins you would use to make each amount. Use as few coins as possible.

a	£2.50	d	£3.60	g	£3.20	j	£1.90
b	80p	e	£1.25	h	£4.15	k	£3.78
c	£4.25	f	£2.70	i	£2.02	l	£4.69

2 Find the change from £5 if you buy these items.

a magazine £2.75   g T-shirt £4.17
b cassette tape £3.95   h candles £1.82
c pencil case £1.75   i fast food £2.84
d ice creams £3.70   j computer game £4.31
e book £2.99   k make-up £3.78
f sunglasses £3.15   l cinema ticket £2.92

TALKING POINT

There are 100 pence in one pound.
100p = £1

There are 100 cents in one dollar.
100¢ = $1

There are 100 cents in one euro.
100¢ = 1€

Is it the same for all currencies?

C **1** Change these amounts from pounds to pence.

a	£1	d	£1.50	g	£1.90	j	£5.75
b	£3	e	£2.50	h	£2.75	k	£4.19
c	£8	f	£6.50	i	£4.60	l	£2.04

2 Change these amounts from pence to pounds.
   a 100p   **d** 450p   **g** 375p   **j** 175p
   b 200p   **e** 350p   **h** 420p   **k** 108p
   c 400p   **f** 250p   **i** 342p   **l** 205p

3 Change these amounts from pounds to pence.
   a £0.25   **d** £0.15   **g** £0.31   **j** £0.04
   b £0.50   **e** £0.85   **h** £0.48   **k** £0.19
   c £0.75   **f** £0.65   **i** £0.69   **l** £0.09

4 Change these amounts from pence to pounds.
   a 80p   **d** 90p   **g** 82p   **j** 4p
   b 45p   **e** 35p   **h** 74p   **k** 2p
   c 20p   **f** 15p   **i** 18p   **l** 12p

5 Write these amounts in order, smallest first.
   a 24p, £0.10, £0.65, 45p, £0.32
   b £0.72, £0.13, 26p, 14p, £1.40
   c 69p, 96p, £0.06, £1.96, £0.70
   d 88p, £0.68, 48p, £0.78, 8p
   e £2.74, £0.36, £3.60, 275p, 48p

JUST DO IT!

Look at the prices in a supermarket or a music store.

How much is 1 CD to the nearest pound (£)?

Why does the shop charge £11.99 and not £12?

Make a poster of supermarket costs.
Use labels and packaging and the price.
Estimate the cost of 2, 3 or 4 of the same item by rounding to the nearest pound or 10p.

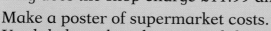

CDs CDs CDs
CDs
£11.99
CDs CDs
CDs, CDs, C

D Use a calculator for these questions.

1 Write each answer in both pence and in pounds.
   a 3 × 25p   **d** 4 × 45p   **g** 5 × 27p
   b 4 × 50p   **e** 13 × 7p   **h** 17 × 30p
   c 5 × 40p   **f** 20 × 50p   **i** 40 × 3p

2 Write each answer in both pence and in pounds.
   a £5.00 ÷ 4   **d** £3.25 ÷ 5   **g** £6.25 ÷ 25
   b £6.00 ÷ 5   **e** £1.70 ÷ 2   **h** £7.50 ÷ 25
   c £2.00 ÷ 5   **f** £1.69 ÷ 13   **i** £11.28 ÷ 4

3 Add these amounts without a calculator.
Check your answers with a calculator.
Write your answers in both pounds and in pence.
a 4p + 22p + 7p + 9p
b 18p + 27p + 11p + 12p
c 42p + 16p + 8p + 14p
d 72p + 26p + 19p + 19p
e 48p + 37p + 52p + 24p

4 Find the answer to each subtraction without a calculator.
Check your answer with a calculator.
Write your answers in both pounds and in pence.
a 80p − 17p   **d** 62p − 15p   **g** £2.75 − £1.62
b 68p − 22p   **e** 98p − 79p   **h** £3.50 − 50p
c 45p − 25p   **f** £1.24 − £1.04   **i** £4.25 − 50p

5 These calculator displays show amounts in pounds. Write each one in words.

a 0.42   **d** 2.45   **g** 1.5

b 0.89   **e** 3.27   **h** 10.4

c 1.57   **f** 1.82   **i** 0.8

E Use a calculator for these questions.
When someone dies they often leave money to friends and relatives.

1 In each question work out how much money each person should have.
Decide what to do with any remainders.
a Mrs Smith leaves £200 to Sarah, Paul, John and Sue.
b Uncle Silas leaves £150 to Martha, Mary-Lou, Jock, Alan and Pete.
c Susie Wong leaves £100 to Matt, Filip, Angela and Betty.
d Grandma Jackson leaves £125 to Claire, Oswald, Harry, Jack and Imogen.
e Mr Patel leaves £175 to Diana, Mahesh and Lisa.

2 How much does Aunty Phyllis leave if Petra, Leanne and Daryl get £82 each?

REVISION

FACT

There are 100 pence in one pound.
100p = 1

LEARNING TIPS

Remember to add the 0 when you get answers like this on your calculation
4.5 → £4.50 → 450 p
0.6 → £0.60 → 60 p

Remember to estimate costs by rounding.
£1.99 → £2.00
49 p → 50 p
£4.69 → £4.70

CHECK IT OUT

1 Write down the amount in each pile.

a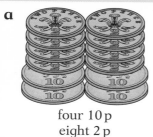
four 10 p
eight 2 p

b
five 50 p
three 20 p

2 Find out how much money is in each pile.
Write the amounts in order, smallest first.

four 20 p   two 50 p   three 5 p   one 20 p
                                two 10 p   one 50 p

3 Choose the coins you would use to make these amounts.
Use as few coins as possible.
a 43 p   b £1.72   c £4.80

4 Find the change from £5 when you buy
a a magazine costing £2.99   c 4 pens costing 12 p each.

5 Change these amounts from pounds to pence.
a £3.20   b £0.08

6 Change these amounts from pence to pounds.
a 182 p   b 19 p

CHECK IT OUT

7 Use a calculator to work out these.
Write your answers in both pounds and in pence.
a 5 × 20p   **c** £1.75 ÷ 5
b 6 × 48p   **d** £2.24 ÷ 4

8 Work out these amounts without a calculator.
Check your answers using a calculator.
a 42p + 69p + 38p + 12p   **b** £1.75 − 69p

9 Mr Jones leaves £180 to Paula, Brian, Neil and Denise.
How much do they each receive?

3.8 PLACE VALUE, ADDITION AND SUBTRACTION, MENTAL MATHS

FACT

The number 8 is a **digit**.
Where you place it determines what it is worth.

H	T	U		H	T	U		H	T	U
		8				8				8
		↓				↓				↓

worth **8**　　　　　　worth **80**　　　　　　worth **800**

A

1 What is the 4 worth in each number?

    a 240　　　　**c** 384　　　　**e** 491　　　　**g** 407

    b 422　　　　**d** 142　　　　**f** 347　　　　**h** 114

2 What is the 7 worth in each number?

    a 107　　　　**c** 347　　　　**e** 997　　　　**g** 765

    b 272　　　　**d** 750　　　　**f** 676　　　　**h** 474

3 What is the 1 worth in each number?

    a 105　　　　**c** 391　　　　**e** 210　　　　**g** 123

    b 201　　　　**d** 159　　　　**f** 417　　　　**h** 91

4 Work out the answer to each of these.
Write down the digit in the tens column.

    a 14 + 69　　　　**c** 148 − 61　　　　**e** 596 + 217

    b 124 + 32　　　　**d** 275 − 80　　　　**f** 352 + 104

5 Work out the answer to each of these.
Write down the digit in the hundreds column.

    a 104 + 328　　　　**c** 211 + 472　　　　**e** 782 − 569

    b 97 + 249　　　　**d** 629 − 14　　　　**f** 309 − 122

6 Work out the answer to each of these.
Write down the digit in the units column.

    a 241 + 19　　　　**c** 457 + 35　　　　**e** 984 − 111

    b 48 + 62　　　　**d** 100 − 64　　　　**f** 836 − 94

JUST DO IT!

H T U
5 5 5 has the same digit in the hundreds, tens and units columns.

Find 9 more ways of making 555 by adding.
Write each addition in a spider diagram like this one.

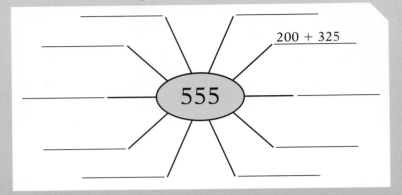

Draw another spider diagram for 222.
Find 10 ways of making 222 by adding.

TALKING POINT

You can choose a method of adding numbers that works for you.
Which of these methods do *you* use to find

    34 + 87?

method 1
    H T U
        3 4
    + ₁ 8₁ 7
    ──────────
      1 2 1

method 2
34 + 80 = 114   7 left to add
114 + 6 = 120   1 left to add
120 + 1 = 121

B **1** Use *method 2* to work out the answers to these.

a 42 + 38   d 104 + 45   g 351 + 15
b 59 + 11   e 75 + 26   h 243 + 78
c 75 + 35   f 210 + 68   i 268 + 74

2 Use *method 1* to work out the answers to these.

a 19 + 50   d 125 + 32   g 348 + 26
b 27 + 44   e 274 + 17   h 296 + 40
c 93 + 26   f 108 + 47   i 315 + 91

TALKING POINT

You can choose a method of subtracting a number that works for you.
Which of these methods do *you* use to find

$174 - 38$?

method 1

```
  H T U
  ⁶1 7 ¹4
−    3 8
  1 3 6
```

method 2

$174 - 30 = 144$ 8 left

$144 - 4 = 140$ 4 left

$140 - 4 = 136$

3   Use *method 2* to work out the answers to these.

a $75 - 12$ **d** $136 - 28$ **g** $425 - 130$

b $88 - 47$ **e** $247 - 39$ **h** $417 - 36$

c $94 - 25$ **f** $350 - 170$ **i** $304 - 174$

4   Use *method 1* to work out the answers to these.

a $59 - 15$ **d** $142 - 31$ **g** $428 - 240$

b $97 - 42$ **e** $252 - 49$ **h** $476 - 182$

c $88 - 39$ **f** $367 - 75$ **i** $313 - 164$

5   Use any method you choose to work these out without a
calculator.

a $48 - 29$ **e** $275 + 90$ **i** $62 + 384$ **m** $194 - 167$

b $72 - 46$ **f** $304 + 87$ **j** $269 + 41$ **n** $438 - 291$

c $128 + 324$ **g** $419 - 50$ **k** $315 + 188$ **o** $324 - 288$

d $404 - 84$ **h** $215 + 149$ **l** $287 - 92$ **p** $246 - 197$

6   Both sides of these calculations give the same answer.
Copy each one and fill in the box.

a $27 + 43 = 100 - \square$ **f** $196 + \square = 100 + 108$

b $200 - 120 = \square + 65$ **g** $500 + 200 = 980 - \square$

c $150 + \square = 400 - 225$ **h** $48 + 315 = 400 - \square$

d $68 + 113 = 58 + \square$ **i** $400 - \square = 470 - 134$

e $120 - 48 = 140 - \square$ **j** $800 - 162 = 480 + \square$

JUST DO IT!

Play these games with a friend.
You need a stopwatch or clock with a second hand.

Add It
Start with 5.
Keep adding 4 for 30 seconds.
Whoever gets the highest correct value wins.
Start with different numbers and different 'add it' values.

Take It
Start with 100.
Keep subtracting 3 for 30 seconds.
Whoever gets the lowest correct value wins.
Start with different numbers and different 'take it' values.

C Work these out mentally.
Try to be as quick and accurate as you can.

1 a 38 + 7   e 62 + 9   i 75 + 25   m 70 + 32
   b 26 + 9   f 78 + 8   j 82 + 18   n 80 + 48
   c 42 + 10   g 94 + 6   k 36 + 24   o 90 + 36
   d 34 + 11   h 83 + 16   l 42 + 38   p 60 + 52

2 a 4×8 e 6×5 i 3×10 m 9×3
   b 3×4 f 7×10 j 4×5 n 8×2
   c 9×2 g 3×6 k 6×3 o 6×4
   d 5×3 h 4×10 l 7×2 p 5×6

3 a 20 − 8   e 80 − 30   i 64 − 20   m 40 − 17
   b 30 − 6   f 75 − 15   j 75 − 25   n 30 − 22
   c 50 − 12   g 28 − 12   k 80 − 35   o 50 − 48
   d 60 − 20   h 24 − 15   l 29 − 15   p 60 − 37

4 a 20 ÷ 2   e 10 ÷ 2   i 18 ÷ 3   m 20 ÷ 10
   b 10 ÷ 5   f 25 ÷ 5   j 9 ÷ 3   n 14 ÷ 2
   c 15 ÷ 3   g 16 ÷ 4   k 24 ÷ 4   o 30 ÷ 5
   d 12 ÷ 4   h 12 ÷ 3   l 18 ÷ 2   p 16 ÷ 2

REVISION

Where you place a **digit** determines what it is worth.

H	T	U		H	T	U		H	T	U
		3				3				3
		↓				↓				↓
	worth **3**				worth **30**				worth **300**	

LEARNING TIPS

Write a list of 5 numbers between 10 and 900. Rewrite them in order, smallest first

Check the digit in the hundreds column, then the tens column and finally the units column to find out which number is the largest

Say numbers out loud to help you understand the value of each digit: 283 – "two *hundred* and *eighty*-three"

CHECK IT OUT

1   What is the 2 worth in each number?
   a 204   **b** 128   **c** 299   **d** 502

2   Work out each answer. Write down the digit in the hundreds column.
   a 400 + 38   **b** 350 − 125   **c** 82 + 95

3   Use two different methods to find the answer to each calculation.
   a 127 + 34   **b** 260 − 115   **c** 78 + 26   **d** 400 − 180

4   Both sides of these calculations give the same answer.
   Copy each one and fill in the box.
   a 27 + 13 = 100 − ☐   **b** 250 − 130 = 74 + ☐

5   Work these out mentally.
   a 82 + 17   **c** 8 × 2   **e** 140 + 93   **g** 10 × 7
   b 40 − 27   **d** 30 ÷ 6   **f** 82 − 54   **h** 16 ÷ 4

3.9   NUMBER PROBLEMS

A   Use addition or subtraction to answer each question.

1   Terry is travelling to Atlanta, USA. The time in Atlanta is 5 hours behind the time in the United Kingdom. If it is 8 am in Atlanta what time is it in the UK?

2   An air balloon is flying at 430 metres. It drops by 82 metres.
How high is its new height?

3   Peter spends 39 minutes getting ready for school and 28 minutes getting to school. How long is this altogether?

4   Olivia wants to save £100 towards a trip to France. She saves £19 in the first month, £28 in the second month and £24 in the third month. How much more does she have to save?

5   Chris and Jon go to town. Chris has £10 and Jon has £12. Chris buys a computer magazine for £5.22 and Jon buys some earphones for his mobile phone for £7.69. How much has each boy got left?

6   Lina and Carly have £18.24 between them. Lina has £3.86. How much does Carly have?

7   Nick has £20. He wants to buy a cinema ticket that costs £4.50, popcorn and a drink that cost £3.80, a magazine that costs £5.25 and a fast-food meal that costs £4.29. Will he have enough left for his bus fare that costs £1.25?

8   Jessie is travelling across Europe. Her total distance is 845 miles. She has travelled 679 miles so far. How much further does she have to go?

9   Jake is buying a new outfit with his birthday money.

T-Shirt	sweat top	combat trousers	trainers
£5	£12.50	£18.00	£43

a   How much does Jake's outfit cost?
b   How much would he have left from £100?

10   Yasmin is buying food for lunch.

sandwich	crisps	apple	drink	chocolate bar
£1.95	35 p	20 p	50 p	29 p

a   How much does her lunch cost altogether?
b   How much change does she have from £5?
c   How much would the same lunch cost in total for 5 days?

B   Use multiplication or division to answer each question.

1   a   The seating in an aeroplane is in rows of 7.
How many people can sit in 10 rows?
b   Another aeroplane has seats in rows of 5.
How many rows of chairs will seat 35 people?

2   Stuart buys 8 bars of chocolate. They cost £4.80 in total.
a   Use a calculator to find the cost of one bar of chocolate.
b   How much would 10 bars cost?
c   How many bars could he buy for £7.50?
How much money would he have left over?

3   Phoebe is buying pictures for her bedroom. Each one costs £3.
a   What is the cost of 4 pictures?
b   What is the cost of 5 pictures?
c   What is the cost of 10 pictures?
d   How many pictures can she buy with £36?
(You can use a calculator to work this out.)

4   Matt is cycling around Europe.
a   In the first week he travels 10 miles a day.
How far does he travel?
b   He wants to travel 35 miles in the second week.
How many miles does he travel each day?

5   Fiona is organising a birthday party.
a   Use a calculator to work out how much it costs.
10 bottles of pop at £1 each.
3 packs of paper plates at 50p each.
3 packs of plastic cups at 75p each.
7 packs of crisps at 80p each.
7 packs of sandwiches at £2.50 each.
7 packs of cakes at £1.50 each.
b   Find out how much money she has left from £50.

6   Mr Smith is rearranging the classroom.
He is fitting desks along the wall.
Each desk is 2 metres wide.
The wall is 11 metres long.
a   How many desks fit along the wall?
b   How much space is left?

7   Vicky has a packet of crisps every day. Each pack costs 25p.
a   How many packs can she buy with £2.50?
b   The price goes up by 5p. How many packs can she buy now?

8   Ryan and his 4 friends are organising a holiday.
Their train tickets cost £10 each. Their Youth Hostel costs £20
each per night. How much does it cost them altogether for 1
night and the train fare?

C **1** 23 can be made by adding 5×3 and 4×2.
Find ways of making each of these numbers.

a $17 = 3 \times 3 + \square \times \square$

c $29 = 4 \times \square + \square \times \square$

b $26 = \square \times 3 + \square \times 10$

d $31 = 5 \times \square + 4 \times \square$

e 24 can be made in more than one way.
Find 3 ways of making 24.

2 **a** Travis uses these digits to make 2 numbers.

7   4   1
2   6   3

When the numbers are added together the answer is 383.
Put the digits in the right places to give the correct answer.

$$\begin{array}{ccc} 1 & \square & 7 \\ + \ \square & \square & 6 \\ \hline 3 & 8 & 3 \end{array}$$

b Jervais uses these digits to make 2 numbers.

4   3   5
4   3   2

When the numbers are added together the answer is 579.
Put the digits in the right places to give the correct answer.

$$\begin{array}{ccc} \square & 3 & \square \\ + \ \square & \square & 5 \\ \hline 5 & 7 & 9 \end{array}$$

c Sharon uses these digits to make 2 numbers.

5   1   3
6   2   4

When one number is subtracted from the other the answer is 122.
Put the digits in the right places to give the correct answer.

$$\begin{array}{ccc} 6 & \square & 4 \\ - \ \square & 1 & \square \\ \hline 1 & 2 & 2 \end{array}$$

d Kelly uses these digits to make 2 numbers.

9   1   2
1   4   3

When one number is subtracted from the other the answer is 829.
Put the digits in the right places to give the correct answer.

$$\begin{array}{ccc} \square & 4 & \square \\ - \ 1 & \square & 3 \\ \hline 8 & 2 & 9 \end{array}$$

3 **a** Write down a sequence that goes up in 4s.
The third term is 10.

$\square$, $\square$, 10, $\square$, $\square$, $\square$

b Write down a sequence that goes up in 10s.
The fifth term is 82.

$\square$, $\square$, $\square$, $\square$, 82, $\square$, $\square$

3.10 LANGUAGE OF NUMBER

A   All these words begin with **c** or **d**:

calculator	centimetre	display	count	currency
calculation	cent	divide	column	division
down	digit	dollar		

1   Copy each word and fill in the missing vowels.

a c_nt_m_tr_

b d_v_s__n

c c__nt

d d_wn

e c_rr_ncy

f c_nt

g c_lc_l_t_r

h d_g_t

i c_lc_l_t__n

j c_l_mn

k d_ll_r

l d_v_d_

m d_spl_y

All these words have the same ending: **tion**

addition	reduction	subtraction	solution
multiplication	calculation	fraction	

2   Copy each word and fill in the missing vowels.

a s_l_t__n

b c_lc_l_t__n

c fr_ct__n

d s_btr_ct__n

e _dd_t__n

f m_lt_pl_c_t__n

g r_d_ct__n

B   **1**   Sort these words into 2 categories.
Put them in a table.
Choose your own categories.

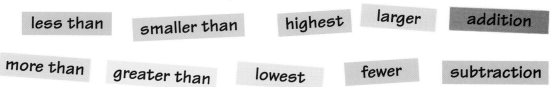

2   Sort these fraction words into 2 categories.
Put them in a table.
Choose your own categories.

3 Sort these money words into 2 categories.
Put them in a table.
Choose your own categories.

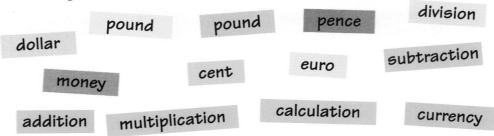

pound   pound   pence   division

dollar

euro   subtraction

money   cent

addition   multiplication   calculation   currency

W C Find the words in the Vocabulary wordsearch.

Vocabulary

```
n f t t s p q b h f
w e f n u t e r m f
t h g z u u m j s z
o i z a l o e y e l
q l m a t a m y q a
e o v e k i y a u u
p o s i t i v e e q
l o b m y s r e n e
y r g l p c e n c f
x x a a s u p p e f
```

amount   sequence
equal   symbol
negative   term
positive   time
puzzle   value

JUST DO IT!

7-Letter Hangman
Play hangman with a friend.
Take it in turns to choose from these words and then
choose some of your own.

sixteen   seconds   pattern   diagrams
minutes   highest   equally   answers
numbers   quarter   smaller   hundred

3.11 CLASSIFICATION

The side of a shape is called an **edge**.
The corner of a shape is called a **vertex**.
More than one corner are called **vertices**.

A

1 a What is the name of this shape?
  b Write down the name of X.
  c Write down the name of Y.

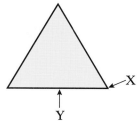

2 a What is the name of this shape?
  b How many edges has got it?
  c How many vertices has it got?

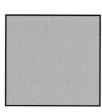

3 a What is the name of this shape?
  b How many edges has it got?
  c How many vertices has it got?

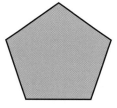

4 a What is the name of this shape?
  b How many edges has got it?
  c How many vertices has it got?

5 a What is the name of this shape?
  b How many edges has it got?
  c How many vertices has it got?

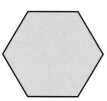

6 a How many edges has this shape got?
  b How many vertices has it got?

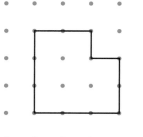

7 a How many edges has this shape got?
b How many vertices has it got?

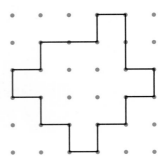

8 Look back at your answers to questions **1–7**.
What do you notice about the number of edges and the number of vertices?

9 On dotty paper draw shapes with the following numbers of edges and vertices.
a 7   **b** 8   **c** 10   **d** 12

FACT

The corner of a solid shape is called a **vertex**.
More than one corner are called **vertices**.
The edge of a solid shape is called an **edge**.
The side of a solid shape is called a **face**.

this shape has **5 vertices**

this shape has **8 edges**

this shape has **5 faces**

---

10 Count the number of edges, vertices and faces for each solid shape.

a 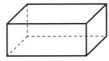   **c**   **e**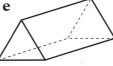

b 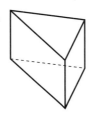   **d** 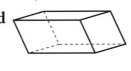   **f**

JUST DO IT!

Collect some food packages and containers.

Count the number of edges, faces and vertices for each package and container.

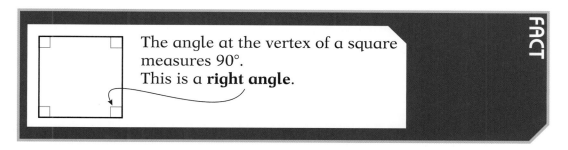

The angle at the vertex of a square measures 90°.
This is a **right angle**.

FACT

ß **1** Write down 'right' or 'not right' for each angle.

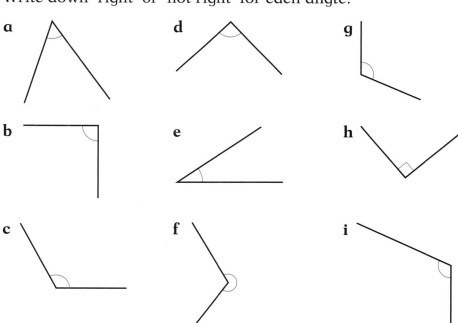

a

b

c

d

e

f

g

h

i

2 Sort these angles into 'angles smaller than a right angle', 'right angles' and 'angles larger than a right angle'.
Put your answers in a table.

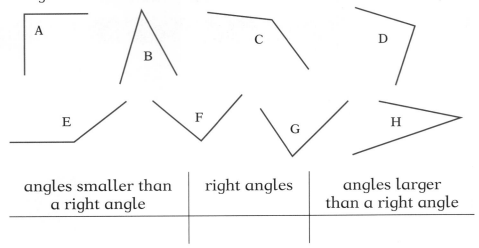

angles smaller than a right angle	right angles	angles larger than a right angle

3 Colour in all the right-angles on this diagram.

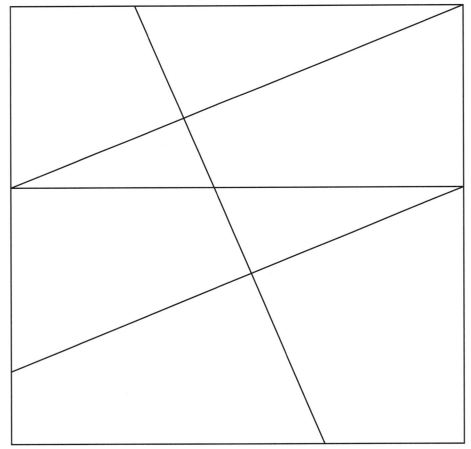

REVISION

FACT

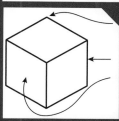

The side of a shape is called an **edge**.

The corner of a shape is called a **vertex**.

More than one corner are called **vertices**.

The corner of a solid shape is called a **vertex**.

More than one corner are called **vertices**.

The edge of a solid shape is called an **edge**.

The side of a solid shape is called a **face**.

LEARNING TIPS

Notice that the numbers of edges and vertices on a 2D shape are the same, but not on a solid 3D shape

Practice drawing shapes on square dotty paper for 2D shapes and on triangular dotty paper for 3D shapes

CHECK IT OUT

1   How many edges and vertices has this shape got?

2   How many faces, edges and vertices has this shape got?

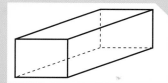

3   Which angle is smaller than a right angle and which angle is larger than a right angle?

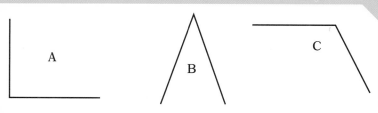

3.12 SYMMETRY

JUST DO IT!

Can you read this message?

What is your name?

Put a mirror at one end of the message and read the message in the reflection.

A **1** Use a mirror to read these messages.
Write each message the correct way round.

a Symmetry means the same

b I love maths

c Four plus three equals seven

d Salad is good for you
Chips are bad for you

e This sentence has been reflected

2 Some letters look the same either way round.
Which of these letters look the same when they are reflected?

c v l w x y p i o s

This shape has 1 line of **reflection symmetry**.

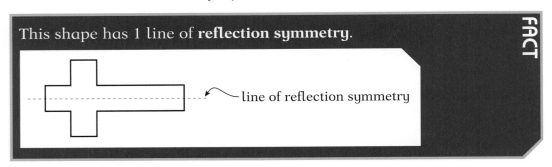

line of reflection symmetry

3 Draw the line of reflection symmetry on each shape.

a

b

c

d

e

f

g

h

i

4   Draw these shapes on squared or dotty paper.
    Draw the line of reflection symmetry on each shape.

a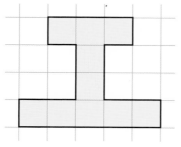

e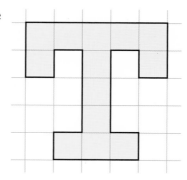

b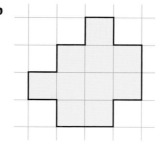

f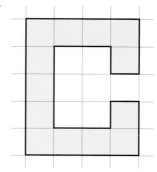

c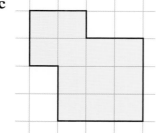

g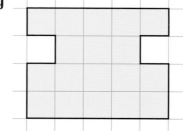

d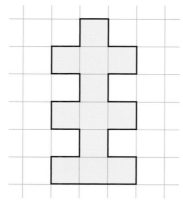

h

5 Copy these shapes onto squared paper or use the worksheet.
    Draw the other half so that each shape has reflection symmetry.

a

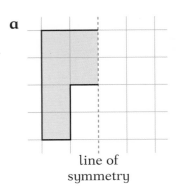

line of
symmetry

c

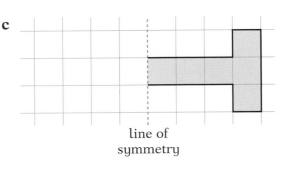

line of
symmetry

b

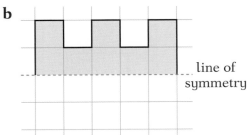

line of
symmetry

d

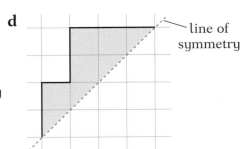

line of
symmetry

6 Use squared paper or dotty paper for this question.
    Draw 3 shapes with 1 line of reflection symmetry.

JUST DO IT!

Find samples of wallpaper. Sort
them into patterns with a line of
reflection symmetry and patterns
without reflection symmetry.

Design your own wallpaper pattern
with reflection symmetry. Use the
computer to copy the pattern. Print
it off in colour.

Some shapes have more than one line of reflection symmetry.   **FACT**

B **1** How many lines of reflection symmetry does each shape have?

a 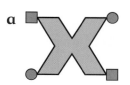   **c**   **e**

b    **d**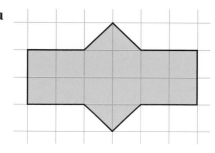

2 How many lines of reflection symmetry does each shape have?

a   **c**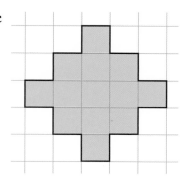

b 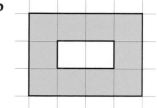   **d**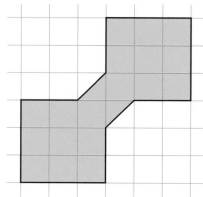

3 Use squared or dotty paper for this question.
Draw 3 shapes with more than 1 line of reflection symmetry.

JUST DO IT!

Use multilink cubes or other cubes that fit together.
You need 6 cubes.

Make as many different shapes as you can with the cubes.

Draw the shapes on triangular dotty paper.

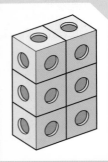

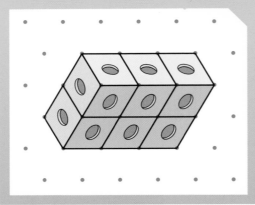

C 1 How many cubes are there in each picture?

a

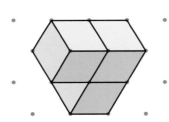

c

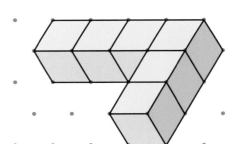

b

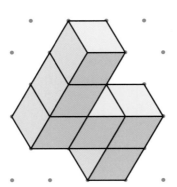

d

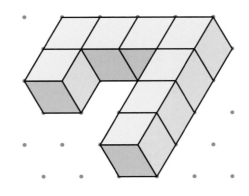

Solid shapes are used in every day objects.

2 **a** Match the shape to the correct name.

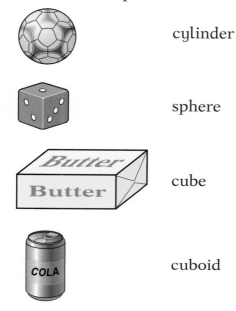

cylinder

sphere

cube

cuboid

b Make a list of foods you find in a cylinder.
c Make a list of foods you find in a cuboid.

REVISION

This shape has 1 line of **reflection symmetry**.

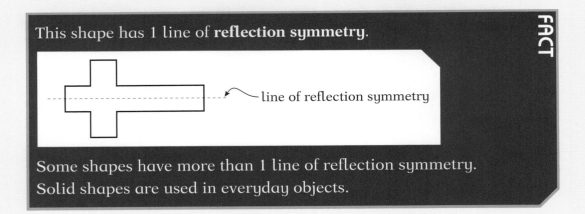

line of reflection symmetry

Some shapes have more than 1 line of reflection symmetry.
Solid shapes are used in everyday objects.

LEARNING TIPS

Use tracing paper to help you

Look at houses. Which types have reflection symmetry – detached, semi-detached or terraced?

Say each syllable of the key words to help you learn how to spell them

CHECK IT OUT

1   Which of these words has reflection symmetry?
    LEVEL   OXO

2   Copy these shapes and draw on the lines of reflection symmetry.

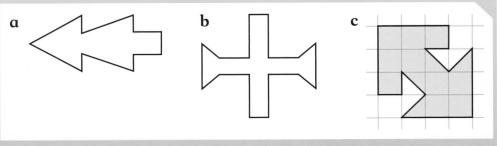

a   b   c

CHECK IT OUT

3 Copy this shape onto squared paper. Draw the other half so the shape has reflection symmetry.

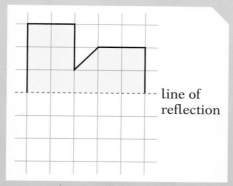

line of reflection

4 What is the name of this solid shape?

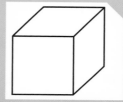

 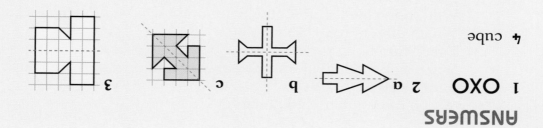

3.13 ANGLES AND TURNING

North pole

South pole

FACT

There are four main **points of the compass**. They give **direction**.

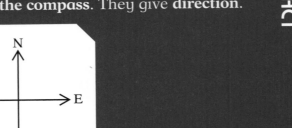

JUST DO IT!

Draw 4 arrows like this on a sheet of paper.
Cut them out.
Cut a piece of A4 paper into 4.
Write North, South, East and West on the pieces.

Lay the arrows and directions on the ground in the same way as the points of the compass and stand in the middle.

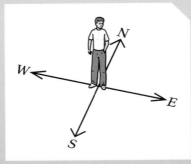

1 Face North.
  Work out which way is clockwise and turn a half turn clockwise.
  Which direction are you facing?
2 Face West.
  Work out which way is anticlockwise and turn a quarter turn anticlockwise.
  Which direction are you facing?

A 1 Gina is using the compass points.
Work out the direction she is facing after each turn.

    a She starts facing North.
      A half turn anticlockwise.

    b She starts facing East.
      A half turn clockwise.

    c She starts facing South.
      A quarter turn clockwise.

    d She starts facing West.
      A quarter turn anticlockwise.

    e She starts facing North.
      A quarter turn clockwise.

    f She starts facing West.
      A three-quarter turn clockwise.

    g She starts facing East.
      A three-quarter turn anticlockwise.

    h She starts facing South.
      A quarter turn anticlockwise.

    i She starts facing East.
      A quarter turn clockwise.

    j She starts facing West.
      A three-quarter turn anticlockwise.

2 Write down the number the arrow points to after each turn.

a A half turn clockwise.

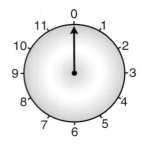

b A quarter turn anticlockwise.

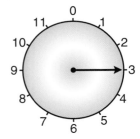

c A half turn anticlockwise.

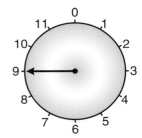

d A quarter turn clockwise.

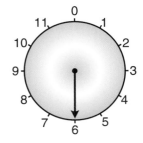

e A three-quarter turn clockwise.

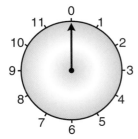

f A three-quarter turn anticlockwise.

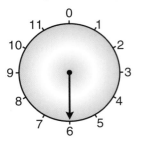

g A half turn clockwise.

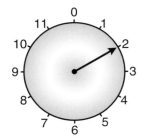

h A half turn clockwise.

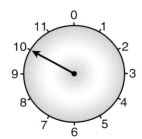

i A quarter turn clockwise.

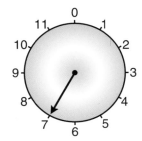

j A quarter turn clockwise.

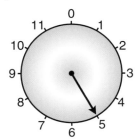

FACT

The angle between each point of the compass measures 90 degrees. It is called a **right angle**.

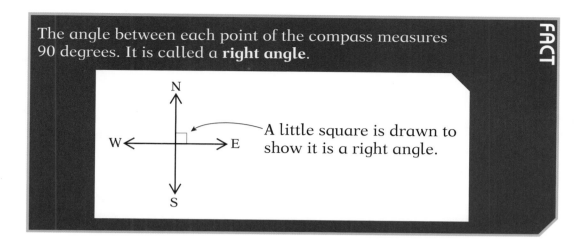

A little square is drawn to show it is a right angle.

JUST DO IT!

You can make a right angle by folding any piece of paper in half twice.

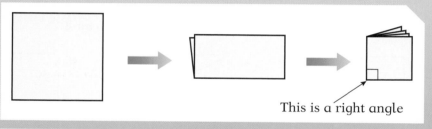

This is a right angle

B **1** Sort these angles into angles measuring a right angle, smaller than a right angle and larger than a right angle.

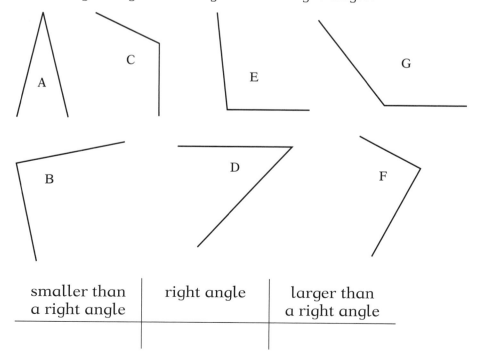

smaller than a right angle	right angle	larger than a right angle

2 Which angle in each shape is a right angle?

a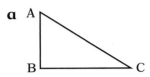

c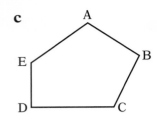

e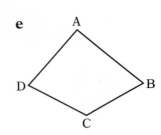

b

d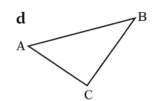

f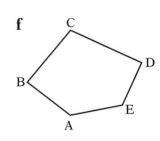

3 How many right angles are there in each shape?

a

c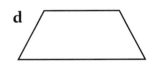

e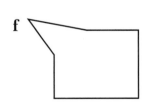

b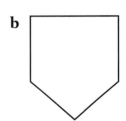

d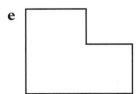

f

JUST DO IT!

Make a square from A4 paper by folding.

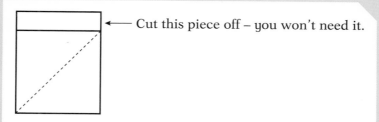

Cut this piece off – you won't need it.

Use a ruler and pencil to draw lines on the square.

Think about the angles you make when you draw the lines.

Try to make some right angles.

Colour each shape a different colour.

Carefully cut out each shape to make a puzzle.

See if your friends can make the pieces back into a square.

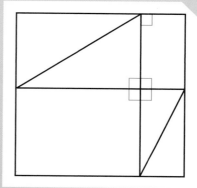

FACT

When two lines never touch or cross they are **parallel**.

C **1** Which pairs of lines are parallel?

a

b

c

d

e

f

g

h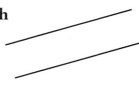

FACT

Lines that are **parallel** are marked with arrows to show they are **parallel**.

2 Draw arrows to show which pairs of lines are parallel.

a

e

b

f

i

c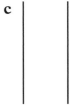

g

j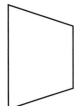

d

h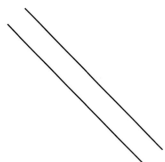

REVISION

There are four main **points of the compass**. They give **direction**.
The angle between each point of the compass measures 90 degrees. It is called a **right angle**. A little square is drawn to show it is a right angle.

When two lines never touch or cross they are **parallel**.
Lines that are parallel are marked with arrows to show they are parallel.

LEARNING TIPS

Look for right angles around the room. Check them with folded paper

The distance between two lines is always the shortest distance you can measure

Notice how many right angles can be joined together at a point

CHECK IT OUT

1 **a** Vince faces North. He turns a three-quarter turn anticlockwise. Which way is he facing?

   b The hand of this dial moves a half turn clockwise.
   Which number is it pointing to?

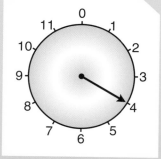

2 Which angle is a right angle?

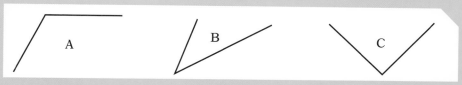

CHECK IT OUT

3 How many right angles are there inside each shape?

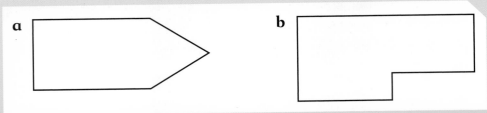

4 Which pairs of lines are parallel?

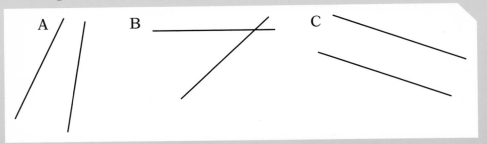

3.14 TIME

Any time from midnight to noon is **am**.
Any time from noon to midnight is **pm**.

A **1** Write these times in order, from the earliest to the latest.

  a 2 pm   3 am   4 pm   1 am

  b 10 pm   7 pm   noon   11 am   6 pm

  c 5 am   1 am   2 pm   midnight   5 pm

  d 9 am   6 pm   3 am   1 am   4 pm

  e 5 pm   4 am   9 am   2 pm   10 pm

  f 8 am   9 pm   10 am   11 pm   noon

  g 7 am   2 am   8 pm   6 pm   9 am

  h 10 pm   3 am   3 pm   7 am   4 am

2 **a** Match the time with the activity for Joseph.
    He works in a shop.

leave for work	7 pm
get up	6 pm
have lunch	8 am
get to work	7 am
get home	1 pm
leave work	9 am
go to bed	11 pm

  b Match the time with the activity for June.
    She works in a factory on the night shift.

have lunch	5 pm
get to work	8 am
get up	4 am
go to bed	6 pm
leave for work	5 am
get home	midnight
leave work	4 pm

c Match the time with the activity for Carly.
She goes to school.

leave for school	7 am
go to bed	7 pm
get up	1 pm
break	8 am
leave school	4 pm
lunchtime	11 am
finish homework	10 pm

d Match the time with the activity for George.
He is retired.

go shopping	8 am
have breakfast	4 pm
get up	9 am
have lunch	5 pm
watch *Countdown*	10 am
go to bed	noon
have dinner	9 pm

JUST DO IT!

Use the Internet or Encarta to find out what 'am' and 'pm' mean.

Some countries use the **24-hour clock** to read time.
You do not use **am** or **pm** with the 24-hour clock.

FACT

B 1 Use the time scale to convert these times from am/pm to the 24-hour clock.

am/pm	24-hour clock
midnight	00.00
1 am	01.00
2 am	02.00
3 am	03.00
4 am	04.00
5 am	05.00
6 am	06.00
7 am	07.00
8 am	08.00
9 am	09.00
10 am	10.00
11 am	11.00
noon	12.00
1 pm	13.00
2 pm	14.00
3 pm	15.00
4 pm	16.00
5 pm	17.00
6 pm	18.00
7 pm	19.00
8 pm	20.00
9 pm	21.00
10 pm	22.00
11 pm	23.00

   a 5 am
   b 10 pm
   c 3 am
   d noon
   e 11 pm
   f 9 am
   g 10 am
   h 4 pm
   i 6 pm

2 Use the time scale to convert these times from the 24-hour clock to am/pm.
   a 02:00
   b 16:00
   c 11:00
   d 23:00
   e 17:00
   f 00:00
   g 04:00
   h 14:00
   i 01:00

3 Write these 24-hour clock times in order, earliest first.
   a 11:00 02:00 16:00 22:00 00:00
   b 07:00 10:00 13:00 08:00 12:00
   c 15:00 11:00 20:00 03:00 04:00
   d 19:00 22:00 15:00 10:00 12:00
   e 03:00 01:00 09:00 10:00 07:00

FACT

There are 60 seconds in 1 minute.
60 sec = 1 min

There are 60 minutes in 1 hour.
60 min = 1 hr

C 1 How many seconds are there in these?
   a 2 min   c 10 min   e $1\frac{1}{2}$ min
   b 5 min   d 4 min   f $\frac{1}{2}$ min

2 How many minutes are there in these?
   a 3 hours   c 10 hours   e $1\frac{1}{2}$ hours
   b 5 hours   d 2 hours   f $\frac{1}{4}$ hour

3 Match the equivalent times.

60 sec	$\frac{1}{2}$ hour
30 min	1 min
120 sec	$1\frac{1}{2}$ hours
90 min	5 min
300 min	2 min
300 sec	5 hours

4 **a** Susie spends 30 minutes washing up, 60 minutes doing homework and 120 minutes watching TV. How many hours is this altogether?

 b Paul spends 60 seconds brushing his teeth, 180 seconds in the shower and 300 seconds getting dressed. How many minutes is this altogether?

 c Cody spends 40 minutes emailing a friend, 30 minutes eating tea and 40 minutes on the phone. How long is this altogether?

 d A bumble bee lands on a rose for 20 seconds, a sunflower for 30 seconds and a buttercup for 30 seconds. How long is this altogether?

JUST DO IT!

Have you ever timed yourself when you do something?

Use a stopwatch or a watch or clock with a second hand to time yourself doing some of these activities.

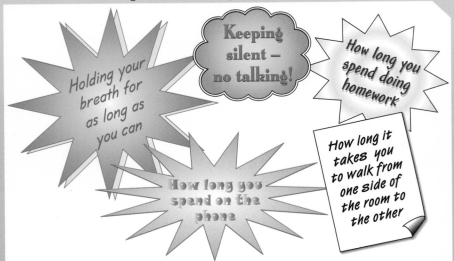

Choose some activities of your own. Put them in a table like this. Illustrate your work with pictures showing what you have done.

Activity	Time taken

D *TV schedule*

BBC 1	ITV 1
7 : 30 EastEnders	7 : 30 Football Match
8 : 00 Holby City	9 : 45 Documentary
9 : 00 In Deep	10 : 45 News and Weather
10 : 00 News and Weather	11 : 15 Music Show
10 : 25 Local News	11 : 45 Comedy Plus
10 : 35 Documentary	
11 : 35 Film Review	

1   EastEnders starts at 7.30 pm and ends at 8.00 pm. How long does the programme?

2   Use the TV schedule to work out how long each of these programmes lasts.
   a Documentary on BBC1.   **e** Documentary on ITV1.
   b News and Weather on ITV1.   **f** Local News on BBC1.
   c News and Weather on BBC1.   **g** In Deep.
   d Holby City.   **h** Football Match.

3   Work out the length of cooking time for each of these meals.
   a *Roast chicken*   **d** *Soup*
         Into the oven at 4.30 pm   Into the pan at   11.20 am
         Cooked at   6.30 pm   Cooked at   11.45 am
   b *Fruit Cake*   **e** *Bread*
         Into the oven at 1.15 pm   Into the oven at 9.25 am
         Cooked at   1.50 pm   Cooked at   10.00 am
   c *Fruit Pie*   **f** *Pizza*
         Into the oven at 10.45 am   Into the oven at 4.45 pm
         Cooked at   11.15 am   Cooked at   5.20 pm

JUST DO IT!

1   Plan a simple meal.

2   Find the cooking time for each recipe.

3   Write a time plan so everything is cooked and ready for 5.30 pm.

MENU

Prawn Cocktail

Vegetable Curry

•

Apple Pie

Chez Susies

REVISION

FACT

Any time from midnight to noon is **am**.
Any time from noon to midnight is **pm**.

Some countries use the **24-hour clock** to read time.
You do not use am or pm with the 24-hour clock.

There are 60 seconds in 1 minute.
60 sec = 1 min
There are 60 minutes in 1 hour.
60 min = 1 hr

LEARNING TIPS

Draw a clock face when you are trying to work out the time difference. Imagine the hands of the clock and count on to the next time

To change time to the 24 hour clock add 12 to the number of hours after noon

CHECK IT OUT

1   Write these times in order, from the earliest to the latest.
    4 am   2 am   2 pm   11 pm   7 pm

2   Convert these times to the 24-hour clock.
    a 3 pm   **b** 10 am   **c** 4 am

3   Convert these times to am/pm.
    a 09:00   **b** 22:00   **c** 11:00

4   How many seconds are there in 4 minutes?

5   How many minutes are there in $2\frac{1}{2}$ hours?

6   How many minutes are 360 seconds?

7   How many hours are 240 minutes?

8   Neighbours starts at 1.45 pm and ends at 2.05 pm.
    How long does it last?

3.15 LENGTHS

TALKING POINT

How many ways of measuring lengths do you know?
How many lengths and heights can you estimate without measuring?

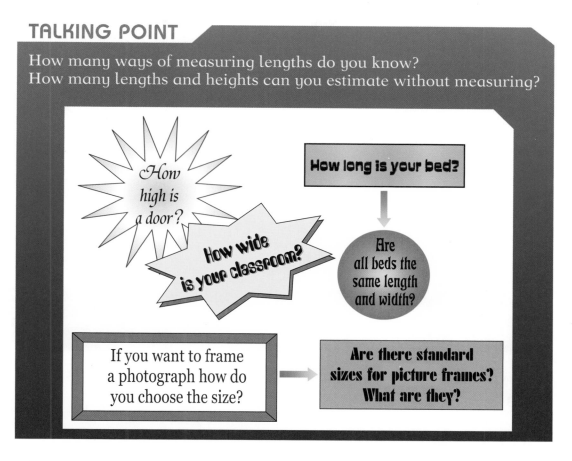

How high is a door?

How wide is your classroom?

How long is your bed?

Are all beds the same length and width?

If you want to frame a photograph how do you choose the size?

Are there standard sizes for picture frames? What are they?

FACT

European countries use **metric** measures.

1000 metres = 1 kilometre

100 centimetres = 1 metre

10 millimetres = 1 centimetre

A **1** Which unit would you choose to measure each item?

a a football pitch   **d** a photo frame

b the height of a chair   **e** the high jump

c the length of a caterpillar   **f** the distance from home to school

JUST DO IT!

1 Cut a plain postcard in half.

2 Make a Metric Measurement Card like this.

3 Keep it in your pocket to help you with measurement questions.

1000 m = 1 km

100 cm = 1 m

10 mm = 1 cm

2 Read the measurement on each ruler or tape measure.

a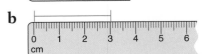

b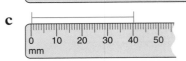

c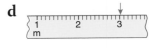

d

e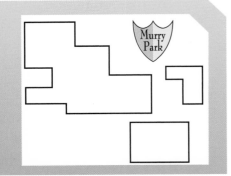

f

g

h

i

j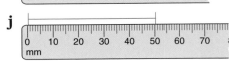

> **FACT**
>
> Always start measuring at 0 on a ruler or tape measure.

Use a ruler to answer these questions.

3 Which is larger?
  a 2 cm or 25 mm?
  b 30 mm or 4 cm?
  c 45 mm or 2 cm?
  d 75 mm or 8 cm?
  e 9 cm or 85 mm?
  f 40 mm or 3 cm?
  g 6 cm or 65 mm?
  h 5 cm or 60 mm?

4 Estimate the length of each line in mm and cm.
      Use your ruler to check your answer.
  a _____
  b _____
  c _____
  d _____
  e _____

JUST DO IT!

Use a plan of your school.

Choose 3 to 5 walls.
Estimate the lengths in metres.

Use a tape or trundle wheel to measure
each wall.

How close were your estimates?

B **1** Match the lengths.

6 cm	4 m
400 cm	9 cm
2000 m	3 km
5 m	40 mm
4 cm	10 m
2 m	2 km
3000 m	60 mm
30 cm	500 cm
90 mm	300 mm
1000 cm	200 cm

2 Write these lengths in order, shortest first.
  a 20 mm, 1 cm, 40 mm, 3 cm, 5 cm
  b 90 mm, 2 cm, 7 cm, 100 mm, 60 mm
  c 80 mm, 3 cm, 6 cm, 70 mm, 20 mm
  d 5 cm, 10 mm, 90 mm, 8 cm, 40 mm
  e 3 cm, 6 cm, 20 mm, 80 mm, 5 cm
  f 2 cm, 15 mm, 4 cm, 25 mm, 7 cm
  g 85 mm, 2 cm, 15 mm, 65 mm, 7 cm

3 Write these lengths in order, shortest first.
  a 4 m, 5 m, 300 cm, 700 cm, 2 m
  b 600 cm, 900 cm, 8 m, 7 m, 500 cm
  c 4 m, 600 cm, 5 m, 100 m, 200 cm
  d 500 cm, 9 m, 800 cm, 4 m, 100 cm
  e 250 cm, 450 cm, 3 m, 9 m, 750 cm
  f 6 m, 500 cm, 850 cm, 350 m, 9 m
  g 650 m, 5 m, 4 m, 550 m, 450 m

4 Write these lengths in order, shortest first.
  a 2 km, 4000 m, 3 km, 1000 m, 5 km
  b 7000 m, 2000 m, 4 km, 5000 m, 2 km
  c 3000 m, 6 km, 4000 m, 9 km, 7000 m
  d 6000 m, 4000 m, 2000 m, 5 km, 1000 m
  e 1500 m, 3 km, 7500 m, 2000 m, 6 km
  f 8 km, 8500 m, 2 km, 2500 m, 7 km
  g 1000 m, 4500 m, 2 km, 6500 m, 4 km

REVISION

FACT

European countries use **metric** measures.

1000 metres = 1 kilometre

100 centimetres = 1 metre

10 millimetres = 1 centimetre

Always start measuring at 0 on a ruler or tape measure.

LEARNING TIPS

Cent means 100 – there are 100 centimetres in 1 metre
Kilo means 1000 – there are 1000 metres in 1 kilometre

Always estimate before you measure

CHECK IT OUT

1 Which unit would you choose to measure each item?
  a the long jump   **b** a car park   **c** the thickness of a book

2 Which is larger?
  a 35 mm or 3 cm?   **b** 400 cm or 3 m?

3 Write these lengths in order, shortest first.
  a 20 mm,   40 mm,   3 cm,   5 cm,   60 mm
  b 300 cm,   2 m,   450 cm,   4 m,   1 m
  c 5 km,   1500 m,   4000 m,   3 km,   6 km

3.16 CALENDAR AND TIMETABLES

JUST DO IT!

Search the Internet for 'Famous Birthdays' or try looking at famousbirthdays.com

All these people were born in January:

Joan of Arc   Elijah Wood   Jackson Pollock
Franklin D. Roosevelt   Edwin 'Buzz' Aldrin

Find out:
a which date and year they were born
b who they are and what they are famous for.

Then:
Find out who else was born on your birthday.

A **1** Work out how old these Kings and Queens of Britain were when they died. Copy and complete the table.

Name	Year born	Year died	Age
Harold II	1022	1066	
Henry VIII	1491	1547	
James I	1566	1625	
Victoria	1819	1901	
Elizabeth I	1533	1603	
Charles II	1630	1685	
George III	1738	1820	

2 Work out how old you will be in
a 2010   **c** 2015   **e** 2050
b 2007   **d** 2030   **f** 2072.

3 Work out the year each person was born. Copy and complete the table.

	Age now	Year born
Scott	20	
Lisa	50	
Wendy	45	
Mabel	70	
Pippa	32	
Maggie	51	
Tilly	5	
Derren	28	

```
1920 —
1930 —
1940 —
1950 —
1960 —
1970 —
1980 —
1990 —
2000 —
2010 —
```

JUST DO IT!

1 Use Microsoft Publisher. Choose 'Calendar' then 'Wallet Size' and design your own mini calendar. Your computer may have a different menu. Choose a calendar that gives a similar calendar to this one.

2 Design other calendars using this program.

2001

January	February	March
M T W T F S S	M T W T F S S	M T W T F S S
1 2 3	1 2 3 4 5 6 7	1 2 3 4 5 6 7
4 5 6 7 8 9 10	8 9 10 11 12 13 14	8 9 10 11 12 13 14
11 12 13 14 15 16 17	15 16 17 18 19 20 21	15 16 17 18 19 20 21
18 19 20 21 22 23 24	22 23 24 25 26 27 28	22 23 24 25 26 27 28
25 26 27 28 29 30 31		29 30 31

April	May	June
M T W T F S S	M T W T F S S	M T W T F S S
1 2 3 4	1 2	1 2 3 4 5 6
5 6 7 8 9 10 11	3 4 5 6 7 8 9	7 8 9 10 11 12 13
12 13 14 15 16 17 18	10 11 12 13 14 15 16	14 15 16 17 18 19 20
19 20 21 22 23 24 25	17 18 19 20 21 22 23	21 22 23 24 25 26 27
26 27 28 29 30	24 25 26 27 28 29 30	28 29 30
	31	

July	August	September
M T W T F S S	M T W T F S S	M T W T F S S
1 2 3 4	1	1 2 3 4 5
5 6 7 8 9 10 11	2 3 4 5 6 7 8	6 7 8 9 10 11 12
12 13 14 15 16 17 18	9 10 11 12 13 14 15	13 14 15 16 17 18 19
19 20 21 22 23 24 25	16 17 18 19 20 21 22	20 21 22 23 24 25 26
26 27 28 29 30 31	23 24 25 26 27 28 29	27 28 29 30
	30 31	

October	November	December
M T W T F S S	M T W T F S S	M T W T F S S
1 2 3	1 2 3 4 5 6 7	1 2 3 4 5
4 5 6 7 8 9 10	8 9 10 11 12 13 14	6 7 8 9 10 11 12
11 12 13 14 15 16 17	15 16 17 18 19 20 21	13 14 15 16 17 18 19
18 19 20 21 22 23 24	22 23 24 25 26 27 28	20 21 22 23 24 25 26
25 26 27 28 29 30 31	29 30	27 28 29 30 31

B Use this calendar to answer these questions.

March 2003

M	T	W	T	F	S	S
					1	2
3	4	5	6	7	8	9
10	11	12	13	14	15	16
17	18	19	20	21	22	23
24	25	26	27	28	29	30
31						

1 Write down the day each date falls on.
  a 22nd March 2003   **d** 31st March 2003
  b 4th March 2003   **e** 9th March 2003
  c 15th March 2003   **f** 23rd March 2003

2 Write down the date of each of the following.
  a the first Saturday in March
  b the third Saturday in March
  c the last day of March
  d the second Tuesday in March
  e the fifth Sunday in March
  f two days before the second Tuesday n March.

3 **a** What day is the 1st of April 2003?
  b What day is the 12th of April 2003?
  c How many days are there in March?

4 This poem is about the days in each month.

> *Thirty days hath September*
> *April, June and November*
> *All the rest have thirty-one*
> *Except February alone*
> *And that has twenty-eight days clear*
> *And twenty-nine in each leap year.*

Copy and complete these tables showing the number of days in each month.

Month	Days
January	
February	
March	
April	
May	
June	

Month	Days
July	
August	
September	
October	
November	
December	

FACT

There are **7 days in 1 week**.
There are **52 weeks in 1 year**.
There are **365 days in 1 year**.

C **1** How many days are there in these?

    a 1 week   **c** 5 weeks   **e** 7 weeks
    b 2 weeks   **d** 10 weeks   **f** 20 weeks

2 If today is Sunday, what will the day be in

    a 1 day   **c** 5 days   **e** 2 weeks
    b 3 days   **d** 1 week   **f** 8 days?

JUST DO IT!

Find a local bus or train timetable.

Use it to plan a journey.

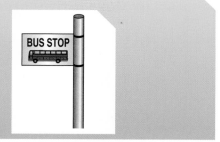

D This timetable shows some American bus times. In America they use the 12-hour clock.

Palm Springs Line 21			
Baristo & Palm Canyon	Tahquitz & Farrell (*Airport*)	San Luis Rey & Ramon	Gene Antrey
6:00 am	6:09 am	6:19 am	6:27 am
7:00 am	7:09 am	7:19 am	7:27 am
8:00 am	8:09 am	8:19 am	8:27 am
9:00 am	9:09 am	9:19 am	9:27 am
10:00 am	10:09 am	10:19 am	10:27 am
11:00 am	11:09 am	11:19 am	11:27 am
12:00	12:09 pm	12:19 pm	12:27 pm
1:00 pm	1:09 pm	1:19 pm	1:27 pm
2:00 pm	2:09 pm	2:19 pm	2:27 pm
3:00 pm	3:09 pm	3:19 pm	3:27 pm
4:00 pm	4:09 pm	4:19 pm	4:27 pm
5:00 pm	5:09 pm	5:19 pm	5:27 pm
6:00 pm	6:09 pm	6:19 pm	6:27 pm
7:00 pm	7:09 pm	7:19 pm	7:27 pm
8:00 pm	8:09 pm	8:19 pm	8:27 pm

1 The bus leaves Baristo & Palm Canyon every hour.
  a What time is the first bus?
  b What time is the last bus?
  c What time is the bus before 1.00 pm?
  d How many buses leave Baristo & Palm Canyon altogether?

2 The bus that leaves Baristo & Palm Canyon at 6.00 am arrives at Tahquitz & Farrell (Airport) at 6.09 am.
  a What time does it arrive at San Luis Rey & Ramon?
  b What time does it arrive at Gene Antrey?
  c How long does it take to get to Tahquitz & Farrell (Airport)?
  d How long is the journey from Baristo & Palm Canyon to Gene Antrey?

3 **a** Where is the bus at 11.09 am?
  b Where is the bus at 2.19 pm?
  c Where is the bus at 4.27 pm?
  d Where is the bus at 7.09 pm?
  e Where is the bus at 7.00 pm?

4 **a** Make arrives at Baristo & Palm Canyon at 1.30 pm. How long does he have to wait for the next bus?
  b Tom arrives at San Luis Rey & Ramon at 5.10 pm. How long does he have to wait for the next bus?
  c Juan arrives at Tahquitz & Farrell (Airport) at 8.05 am. What time does he get to Gene Antrey?
  d Dionne arrives at San Luis Rey & Ramon at 8.45 am. What time does she arrive at Gene Antrey?

This train timetable uses the 24-hour clock.

	1	2	3	4	5	6
Coventry	0603	0733	1103	1203	1533	1931
Birmingham International	0619	0749	1119	1219	1549	1943
Birmingham New Street	0635	0808	1136	1235	1607	1959
Wolverhampton	0702	0833	1200	1300	1632	2024

5   **a** What time does the first train leave Coventry?
   b What time does it arrive at Birmingham International?
   c How long does it take to get to Birmingham International?
   d What time does it arrive at Birmingham New Street?
   e What time does it arrive at Wolverhampton?

6   **a** Which train arrives at Wolverhampton at 1300?
   b Which train arrives at Birmingham New Street at 1607?
   c Which train arrives at Birmingham International at 0749?

REVISION

FACT

There are **7 days in 1 week**.

There are **52 weeks in 1 year**.

There are **365 days in 1 year**.

LEARNING TIPS

Use a clock face like this to help you read timetables which use the 24-hour clock.

To help learn the months of the year, think of which months are in which season or when you play different sports. Think about family birthdays.

CHECK IT OUT

1 Work out how old you will be in 2005 and 2032.

2 Use the March 2003 calendar on p. 179 for these questions.
   a Which day is the 25th March?
   b What is the date of the 3rd Sunday?
   c What day is 3 days after the 11th March?

3 a Which month comes after May?
   b Which month comes before January?

4 How many days are there in 4 weeks?

5 If today is Monday what day will it be in 5 days' time?

6 Use the train timetable on p. 182 to answer these questions.
   a What time does the 4th train arrive at Birmingham New Street?
   b Which train arrives at Wolverhampton at 0833?
   c What time does it leave Coventry?

ANSWERS

2a Tuesday b 16th c Friday 3a June b December 4 28 days 5 Saturday 6a 1235 b 2nd c 0733

3.17 WEIGHT

SLIMQUICK CLUB

Mel is weighing in kilograms (kg).
Has she lost weight this week?
Last week – 58 kg.
This week – 57 kg.

TALKING POINTS

How much does an elephant weigh?
How much does a mouse weigh?
Did people weigh in kilograms in 1900?
How much should you weigh?
Do you need to be able to weigh for some jobs? Which ones?

A   Some of the people in Tara's class are weighed.

   1   Read the weights on each scale. Write down the name and the
   weight.

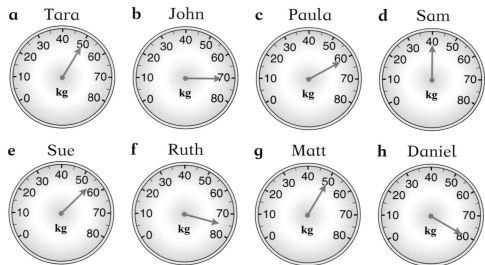

   a   Tara   **b**   John   **c**   Paula   **d**   Sam

   e   Sue   **f**   Ruth   **g**   Matt   **h**   Daniel

   2   Who weighs the heaviest?

   3   Who weighs the lightest?

   4   Who weigh the same?

JUST DO IT!

Contact NHS direct, your local health centre or look on the Internet to find out what is a healthy weight for you.

There are 1000 grams in 1 kilogram.

1000 g = 1 kg

B   Would you choose grams (g) or kilograms (kg) to weigh each of these?

   1 a banana   **4** a chicken

   2 a bag of cement   **5** a ruler

   3 a bag of apples   **6** a birthday cake

C   Do the ingredients weigh more or less than 1 kilogram?

Add them up to find out.

   200 g + 200 g + 200 g + 100 g = 700 g

The ingredients weigh less than 1 kilogram.

Find out whether the ingredients for each recipe weigh more or less than 1 kilogram.

> *Recipe for chocolate biscuits*
> 200 g Flour
> 200 g Sugar
> 200 g Margarine
> 100 g Chocolate

1

> *Pastry*
> 600 g Flour
> 150 g Margarine
> 150 g Lard

3

> *Vegetable Paté*
> 300 g Carrots
> 300 g Onions
> 200 g Beans

5

> *Cheese + Onion Scones*
> 350 g Flour
> 400 g Cheese
> 250 g Margarine
> 200 g Onions

2

> *Lemon Biscuits*
> 600 g Flour
> 300 g Margarine
> 300 g Sugar
> Lemon Juice

4

> *Fruit Scones*
> 200 g Butter
> 300 g Dried Fruit
> 400 g Flour
> 150 g Sugar

6

> *Chicken Mayonnaise*
> 50 g Curry Powder
> 100 g Apricots
> 250 g Mayonnaise
> 500 g Cooked Chicken

JUST DO IT!

Start with [0] on a calculator. Keep inputting [5] [0] [+] until the display is greater than 1000. How many times did it take?
Try again with other numbers

D Read the weight on each scale.

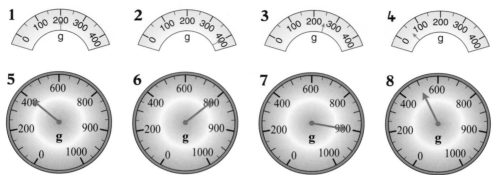

JUST DO IT!

Use scales to find the weights of these.
a a book   **c** a mobile phone   **e** a drink can
b a shoe   **d** a CD   **f** things in your classroom

E Put these weights in order, smallest first.

1   200 g, 150 g, 400 g, 250 g

2   370 g, 430 g, 940 g, 520 g

3   600 g, 580 g, 560 g, 620 g, 680 g

4   305 g, 350 g, 530 g, 330 g, 550 g

5   50 g, 95 g, 25 g, 950 g, 250 g, 500 g

REVISION

1000 grams make 1 kilogram.

1000 g = 1 kg

Can you:
Use scales to weigh?
Read weights?
Choose grams or kilograms correctly?
Put weights in order?

LEARNING TIPS

Practise reading scales and get a friend to check your answers

Go over the questions you got wrong and correct the answers

Weigh lots of things at home

CHECK IT OUT

1   Choose grams or kilograms for weighing each item.
    a a ping pong ball   **b** a bag of sand   **c** mushrooms

2   Read these scales
    a   **b**   **c**

3   Add these weights. Do they total more or less than 1 kilogram?
    a 275 g + 480 g + 250 g   **b** 150 g + 250 g + 400 g + 125 g

4   Put these weights in order, smallest first.

    385 g,   295 g,   420 g,   475 g

3.18 SHAPE, SPACE AND MEASURE PROBLEMS

1 Wayne has 2 hours to complete as many of these activities as he can. Which ones should he do to make the best use of his time?

mend his bike	20 minutes
write to his gran	40 minutes
tidy his bedroom	25 minutes
finish his homework	15 minutes
phone Paul	10 minutes
read his magazine	15 minutes
text a friend	5 minutes
have a shower and get changed	20 minutes
help his sister find her book	5 minutes

W

2 Which of these shapes join together to make a large pattern with no spaces? Use the templates on the worksheet to draw them and find out.

| equilateral triangle | square | regular pentagon | regular octagon | regular hexagon |

3 These are nets of solid shapes. Which solid shapes do they make?

a

b

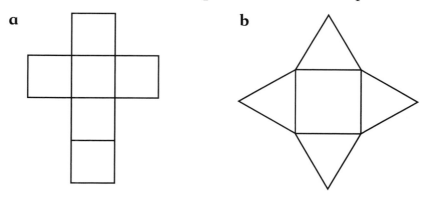

4 Which 4 of these 6 angles when joined together meet at a point without any gaps?

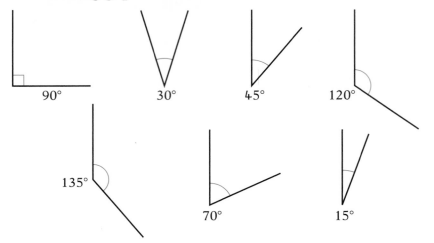

90°   30°   45°   120°

135°   70°   15°

5 a

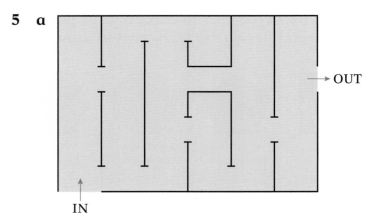

→ OUT

IN

Write instructions to get through the maze.
There is more than one way you can go.
b Design your own maze on squared paper.

6 This recipe is for 20 small cakes.
   a Make a list of the ingredients
      needed to make 100 small cakes.
   b Make a list of the ingredients
      needed to make 5 small cakes.

> *Small Cakes*
> 200 g Self-raising flour
> 200 g Sugar
> 200 g Margarine or Butter
> 4 Eggs

7 Which 4 of these lengths can be added together to make 1 km?
   a 250 m, 300 m, 500 m, 400 m, 950 m, 50 m
   b 125 m, 700 m, 400 m, 600 m, 275 m, 200 m

8 Spencer is twice as old as his sister Donna. Spencer's mum is
20 years older than him and 6 times as old as Donna.
Can you work out how old they all are by guessing?

3.19 LANGUAGE OF SHAPE, SPACE AND MEASURE

An **abbreviation** is a shortened version of a word.

A **1** Write down the full word for each of these abbreviations.

a	Jan	**e**	Jun	**i**	Oct	**m**	min
b	Feb	**f**	Jul	**j**	Nov	**n**	hr
c	Mar	**g**	Aug	**k**	Dec		
d	Apr	**h**	Sept	**l**	sec		

2 Write down the common abbreviation for each of these words.

a	millimetre	**d**	litre	**g**	kilogram	**j**	East
b	centimetre	**e**	millilitre	**h**	North	**k**	West
c	kilometre	**f**	gram	**i**	South		

Singular is one of something.
Plural is more than one of something.

B **1** Write down the plural of each word.

a	square	**e**	vertex	**i**	ruler
b	pentagon	**f**	angle	**j**	weight
c	edge	**g**	cube	**k**	clock
d	face	**h**	cylinder	**l**	time

2 All these words have 'angle' in them:

angle
angles
tri angle
right angle

a Find 3 more words with 'metre' in them.

metre
_ _ _ _ _ metre
_ _ _ _ _ metre
_ _ _ _ metre

b Find 3 more words that end in 'agon'.

_ _ _ _ agon
_ _ _ agon
_ _ _ agon

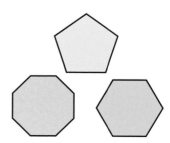

C 1

This word picture illustrates the meaning of two words.

a Draw word pictures for these words:

reflection   parallel   calendar
    shape   ruler   timetable

b Choose some words of your own to draw.

2 Find the words in the Shape and Measure wordsearch.

Shape and Measure

w e i g h t s u s
e s c a l e s m a
g t y h t l a e h
h i a t h r e a m
s m a r g o l i k
s a l e d m o r e
s t s e i v a e h
e e o a e t h j e
l i g h t e s t l

weights	grams	more	healthy
heaviest	kilograms	less	diet
lightest	estimate	scale	

3.20 SORTING AND GRAPHS

JUST DO IT!

Mr Smith is sorting his seeds ready for planting. He sorts them into vegetables and flowers.

1 Find out which of these plants are vegetables and which are flowers. You can use a gardening book or the Internet.

cabbage	daffodil	pansy	rose
geranium	cucumber	kale	leek
aubergine	iris	marigold	carrot
french bean	radish	chrysanthemum	

2 Put the names of the plants into a table like this.

Illustrate your table.
Use Clip Art.

Vegetables	Flowers

A

1 Which of these numbers have been sorted into the wrong columns?

multiples of 3	multiples of 4	multiples of 5
12 33 18 21	9 16 4 8 28	25 35 10 24 50

2 **a** Sort these numbers into the correct columns.

4   30   21   7   10
14   35   50   12   16

multiples of 7	multiples of 10	multiples of 4

b Add some multiples of your own to each column.

191

3 Sort these numbers into the correct columns.

| 10 | 28 | 4 | 25 | 14 | 5 |
| 18 | 15 | 16 | 8 | 20 | 35 |

multiples of only 2	multiples of 2 and 5	multiples of only 5

B **1** Christie has drawn a pictogram.

Favourite TV programmes

EastEnders	
Coronation Street	
Neighbours	
Hollyoaks	

Key: ⬜ represents 2 people

a How many people preferred EastEnders?
b How many people preferred Coronation Street?
c How many people preferred Neighbours?
d How many people preferred Hollyoaks?
e How many people were asked altogether?

2 Jason asked his class what time they went to bed.
He put the results in a pictogram.

Bed times

before 9 pm	
between 9 pm and 10 pm	
betweeen 10 pm and 11 pm	
after 11 pm	

Key: ☽ represents 2 people

a How many people went to bed before 9 pm?
b How many people went to bed between 9 pm and 10 pm?
c How many people went to bed between 10 pm and 11 pm?
d How many people went to bed after 11 pm?
e How many people were asked altogether?

3 Mandy was preparing for a party. She asked her friends what they wanted to drink. She put the answers in a pictogram.

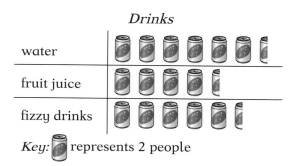

Drinks

water	
fruit juice	
fizzy drinks	

Key: represents 2 people

a How many people wanted water?
b How many people wanted fruit juice?
c How many people wanted fizzy drinks?
d How many people were asked altogether?

4 Lulu asked her friends which type of films they preferred. She put the results in a pictogram.

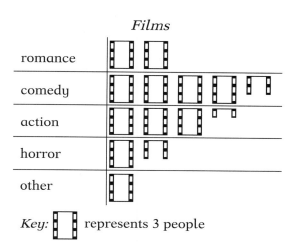

Films

romance	
comedy	
action	
horror	
other	

Key: represents 3 people

a How many people chose action films?
b How many people were asked altogether?
c How many more people preferred romance films to horror films?
d How many more people chose comedy films than romance films?
e Which type of film was the most popular?

5 Daisy asked her friends which was their favourite type of film. Draw a pictogram to show the results.

Use ▮ to represent 3 people.

comedy	action	comedy	action
action	comedy	horror	action
horror	action	horror	romance
romance	action	action	action
action	romance	action	action
comedy	romance	comedy	comedy

6 Paul asked his friends what time they went to bed.
Draw a pictogram to show the results.

Use (to represent 2 people.

8 pm	10.05 pm	8.30 pm	11.45 pm
11.05 pm	10.30 pm	9.30 pm	9.10 pm
9.30 pm	8 pm	9.45 pm	10.05 pm
10.20 pm	10.55 pm	8.45 pm	8.45 pm
10.40 pm	11.30 pm	9.15 pm	11.15 pm

7 Darius made a list of his friends' favourite sports.
Put the results in a pictogram.
Choose your own symbol to represent 4 people.

football	cricket	rugby	swimming
football	rugby	football	cricket
football	cricket	football	football
swimming	rugby	swimming	football
cricket	swimming	football	cricket
football	football	football	cricket
football	football	cricket	football
cricket	football	football	football

JUST DO IT!

1 Ask 20 people their favourite sweets.

2 Choose your own symbol to represent 2 people.

3 Draw a pictogram showing your results.

C 1 Tyrone has drawn a
bar-chart from his survey.
He asked his friends if they
preferred listening to music,
watching TV, going to the
cinema or reading a book.

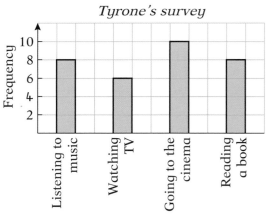

Tyrone's survey

a How many friends chose 'listening to music'?
b How many friends chose 'watching TV'?
c How many friends chose 'going to the cinema'?
d How many friends chose 'reading a book'?
e How many friends were asked altogether?

2 Scott drew a bar-chart showing the results of his survey to find out his friends' favourite fruit.

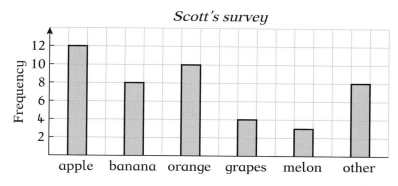

Scott's survey

a How many people preferred grapes?
b How many people preferred apples?
c Did more people prefer melon or bananas?
d How many people were there in the survey altogether?
e How many people preferred oranges or apples?

3 Sophie drew a bar-chart showing the results of her survey to find out the colour of her friends' favourite T-shirts. She put the results in a bar-chart.

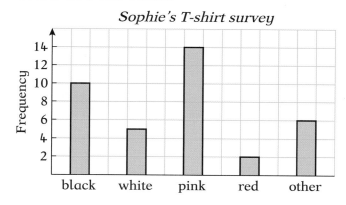

Sophie's T-shirt survey

a How many people did Sophie ask?
b How many more people preferred pink than white?
c Which was the least favourite colour?
d How many people preferred black?

4 Susannah carried out a survey to find her friends' favourite T-shirt colour. Draw a bar-chart to show her results.

pink	black	pink	pink	black
white	blue	white	white	pink
green	white	black	white	pink
white	black	pink	red	red
pink	black	white	green	green
pink	pink	pink	black	black
black	pink	black	pink	yellow

5 **a** Darren carried out a survey to find out which subject his
friends liked the least. Draw a bar-chart showing his results.

French	English	French	English	English
Maths	Science	English	English	Science
French	Maths	Science	French	English
English	English	English	French	Maths
French	Science	Science	English	English
English	French	Science	Maths	English
English	English	Maths	English	French

b Ask the people in your class their least favourite subject.
Draw a bar-chart to show the results.

JUST DO IT!

Newspapers use graphs and charts on the
financial pages.

1 Collect some newspapers.

2 Cut out all the graphs.

3 Sort these graphs into different types.
Make them into a poster.

4 Write at least one sentence to describe each type of graph.

Fuel prices up

REVISION

FACT

A **pictogram** has a key and a title
A **bar-chart** has a title.

LEARNING TIPS

Draw axes going up in equal amounts

Add all the heights of the bars to find the total frequency

You can draw both pictograms and bar-charts when you do a survey

CHECK IT OUT

1 Which numbers are in the wrong columns?

multiples of 4	multiples of 5	multiples of 6
5 4 8	10 25 20	42 6
16 28	35 18	

2 a How many people chose black?
   b How many people chose red?
   c How many people were asked altogether?

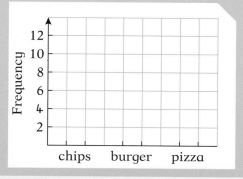

Favourite colour

green
red
blue
black

Key: ⬦ represents 2 people

3 Draw a bar-chart for these favourite foods.

chips	pizza	chips	chips
pizza	chips	chips	burger
pizza	pizza	pizza	pizza
burger	chips	pizza	chips
burger	chips	chips	burger
pizza	pizza	pizza	burger
burger	pizza	burger	chips

Frequency (12, 10, 8, 6, 4, 2)

chips   burger   pizza

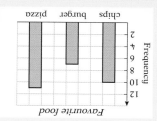

3.21 PROBABILITY

TALKING POINT

Some events are more likely than others.

Some illnesses run in families. Your genetic make-up can determine how likely you are to suffer a particular illness.

Find out about genetic illnesses.

A

1   Write each event in order, from least likely to most likely.

 a You will wake up tomorrow at:
     11 am   4 am   7 am   5 pm

 b Today you will use your mobile to text:
     18 times   100 times   4 times   122 times

 c You will eat chips:
     twice this week   5 times this week   3 times this week

2   Wayne plays darts.
   His previous scores have been:
       150   120   91   120   57   120

   Write the following scores in order from least likely to most likely for Wayne's next turn:
       120   48   180   5

3   Mrs Clarke collects money for charity in the High Street.
   Last week's collection

Monday	Tuesday	Wednesday	Thursday	Friday
£12.83	£17.45	£11.19	£18.52	£15.53

   Write these amounts in order from the least likely to the most likely for Mrs Clarke's next collection:
       £30.10   £18.25   5p   £8.20

FACT

You can show **probability** on a scale.

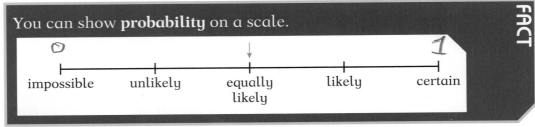

impossible   unlikely   equally likely   likely   certain

ß

W

Mark an arrow on a probability scale like this to show how likely each outcome is.

impossible   unlikely   equally   likely   certain
                                   likely

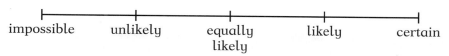

1   If you throw a coin you will get a tail.

2   Next time you visit the dentist you will have a filling.

3   Tomorrow night you will watch EastEnders.

4   You will buy a CD on Saturday.

5   You will go to the cinema on Monday.

6   Your mobile phone will ring tonight.

7   Your dad will give you £100 on Sunday.

8   You will have your hair cut before June 21st.

9   If May 30th is a Saturday then May 31st will be a Sunday.

10   February 29th will be your birthday.

11   Write down 3 things that are impossible.

12   Write down 3 things that are unlikely.

13   Write down 3 things that are equally likely.

14   Write down 3 things that are likely.

15   Write down 3 things that are certain.

JUST DO IT!

People bet on horses to win races.
They decide how likely they are to win based on previous races. This is called **form**.

1   Look at the racing pages of a daily newspaper.

2   Choose a horse from each race by looking at their previous form.

3   Try to find out if your chosen horses win their races.

TALKING POINT

Betting on horses to win races is a type of gambling.

What other sorts of gambling do you know?

How old do you have to be to gamble?

What are the dangers of gambling?

FACT

To be **fair** every outcome must have an equal chance.

C *Dice Games*
Choose which dice games are fair. Each player must have the same chance of winning. Write down 'fair' or 'not fair'.

1   Using a 6-sided dice, John wins if he rolls a 1, 2 or 3. Peter wins if he rolls a 4, 5 or 6.

2   Using a 6-sided dice, Kylie wins if she rolls a 2, 4 or 6. Chantelle wins if she rolls a 1, 3 or 5.

3   Using a 6-sided dice, Tariq wins if he rolls a 3, 4, 5 or 6. Dominic wins if he rolls a 1 or 2.

4   Using a 6-sided dice, Fiona wins if she rolls a 2 or 5. Latifa wins if she rolls a 1 or 4.

5   Using a 6-sided dice, Ali wins if he rolls a 1, Alex wins if he rolls a 2 or 3 and Steven wins if he rolls a 4, 5 or 6.

6   Using a 6-sided dice, Chris wins if she rolls a 2 or 4, Annie wins if she rolls a 1 or 6 and Jaye wins if she rolls a 3 or 5.

7   Using a 10-sided dice, Dean wins if he rolls any number from 1 to 6. Aaron wins if he rolls any number from 7 to 10.

8   Using a 10-sided dice, Scott wins if he rolls a 1, 4, 5, 7 or 9. Guru wins if he rolls a 2, 3, 6, 8 or 10.

JUST DO IT!

Make your own dice game using a 6-sided dice or a 10-sided dice.

Decide which numbers you need to win.

Do you always lose if you make the game unfair?

REVISION

FACT

You can show **probability** on a scale.

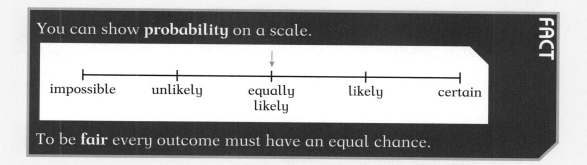

impossible   unlikely   equally likely   likely   certain

To be **fair** every outcome must have an equal chance.

LEARNING TIPS

Make a record of the time you get to school each day. How likely is it you will be 10 minutes early?

Throw a coin 40 times. Write down the results. Did you get 20 heads and 20 tails?

Think of as many things that are certain as you can

CHECK IT OUT

1 Write these events from least to most likely.
   Between 9 am and 3 pm you will talk:

   5 times   once   100 times   70 times

2 Draw a probability scale. Put an answer to show how likely it is that your friend will give you £20 tonight.

3 Write down two things that are very likely.

4 Using a 6-sided dice, Anthony wins if he rolls a 1, 5 or 6. Danny wins if he rolls a 2, 3 or 4. Is this game fair?

4 Yes

ANSWERS

4.1 MENTAL MATHS

JUST DO IT!

Use a stopwatch to time yourself.

1 Start with 2 and keep adding on 3 for 30 seconds. Write down the number you get to. Do it again. Try and improve your score each time.

Do the same for each of these questions.

2 Start with 5 and keep adding on 4 for 30 seconds.

3 Start with 4 and keep adding on 3 for 30 seconds.

4 Start with 7 and keep adding on 4 for 30 seconds.

A

1 Add these numbers without a calculator.

   a 8 + 7
   d 11 + 22
   g 16 + 21 + 3

   b 9 + 4
   e 15 + 8
   h 19 + 5 + 4

   c 10 + 11 + 9
   f 27 + 9
   i 9 + 8 + 7

2 Find out which calculation gives the largest answer.

   a 21 + 42 or 53 − 9
   d 34 + 47 or 92 − 15

   b 44 + 12 or 74 − 30
   e 27 + 44 or 162 − 40

   c 19 + 13 or 60 − 25
   f 38 + 39 or 85 − 29

3 Subtract these numbers without a calculator

   a 60 − 51
   d 50 − 27
   g 36 − 9 − 8

   b 88 − 17
   e 74 − 19
   h 52 − 12 − 5

   c 95 − 24
   f 84 − 25
   i 74 − 20 − 14

4 Find out which calculation gives the largest answer.

   a 50 − 17 or 60 − 28
   d 84 − 35 or 71 − 24

   b 38 − 19 or 47 − 28
   e 55 − 37 or 62 − 41

   c 100 − 52 or 91 − 24
   f 95 − 19 or 49 − 24

5 Suki has £2. Has Suki got enough money to buy each of these?

   a 5 packets of sweets at 50 p each

   b 4 drinks at 60 p each

   c 3 kilos of apples at 60 p a kilo

   d 6 packets of biscuits at 40 p each

   e 7 pencils at 25 p each

   f 6 bus tickets at 35 p each

ß Buses and trains often run at regular times.
Find the next 5 bus times for each route.

1 *Route A*
every 5 minutes
09:05
09:10
⋮

2 *Route B*
every 10 minutes
08:20
08:30
08:40
⋮

3 *Route C*
every 15 minutes
07:20
07:35
⋮

4 *Route D*
every 3 minutes
10:24
10:27
10:30
⋮

5 Route E
every 4 minutes
16:41
16:45
⋮

6 Route F
every 7 minutes
11:20
11:27
⋮

JUST DO IT!

How many ways can you make 10 by
multiplying and adding?

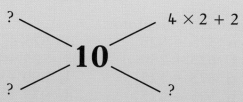

How many ways can you make 8 by
multiplying and subtracting?

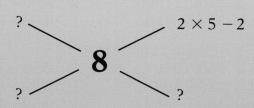

C 1 Find the missing numbers in these flow charts.

  a $\square \longrightarrow \times 2 \longrightarrow + 4 \longrightarrow 18$

  b $4 \longrightarrow \times \square \longrightarrow - 4 \longrightarrow 8$

  c $5 \longrightarrow \times 3 \longrightarrow + \square \longrightarrow 30$

  d $6 \longrightarrow \times 5 \longrightarrow - 8 \longrightarrow \square$

  e $\square \longrightarrow \times 7 \longrightarrow - 2 \longrightarrow 40$

  f $5 \longrightarrow \times \square \longrightarrow - 14 \longrightarrow 16$

  g $2 \longrightarrow \times 12 \longrightarrow - \square \longrightarrow 19$

  h $17 \longrightarrow \times 3 \longrightarrow - 2 \longrightarrow \square$

2 Find the missing numbers in these flow charts.

  a $\square \longrightarrow \div 3 \longrightarrow + 5 \longrightarrow 15$

  b $12 \longrightarrow \div \square \longrightarrow + 7 \longrightarrow 10$

  c $60 \longrightarrow \div 6 \longrightarrow + \square \longrightarrow 40$

  d $18 \longrightarrow \div 3 \longrightarrow + 11 \longrightarrow \square$

  e $\square \longrightarrow \div 5 \longrightarrow - 4 \longrightarrow 7$

  f $24 \longrightarrow \div \square \longrightarrow - 3 \longrightarrow 0$

  g $22 \longrightarrow \div 2 \longrightarrow - \square \longrightarrow 3$

  h $100 \longrightarrow \div 5 \longrightarrow - 17 \longrightarrow \square$

D 1 Add these numbers without a calculator.

a 200 + 300	**e** 800 + 300	**i** 650 + 150
b 400 + 500	**f** 700 + 400	**j** 950 + 250
c 500 + 500	**g** 900 + 800	**k** 850 + 450
d 700 + 300	**h** 750 + 150	**l** 750 + 650

2 Add these numbers without a calculator.

a 275 + 125	**e** 375 + 425	**i** 675 + 325
b 325 + 225	**f** 625 + 250	**j** 525 + 675
c 175 + 275	**g** 875 + 125	**k** 650 + 875
d 350 + 125	**h** 525 + 425	**l** 975 + 875

3 Subtract these numbers without a calculator.

a 400 − 200	**e** 1100 − 400	**i** 3600 − 2900
b 800 − 500	**f** 1200 − 500	**j** 4200 − 1500
c 700 − 600	**g** 2700 − 1800	**k** 3400 − 1700
d 900 − 300	**h** 3500 − 2600	**l** 9800 − 4900

4 Subtract these numbers without a calculator.

a 400 − 150	**e** 950 − 650	**i** 3550 − 550
b 600 − 350	**f** 750 − 300	**j** 2750 − 650
c 850 − 200	**g** 1000 − 650	**k** 2850 − 1250
d 750 − 300	**h** 1200 − 250	**l** 3000 − 1750

REVISION

LEARNING TIPS

When you buy snacks in a shop add the prices in your head *before* you buy

Start with any number and keep subtracting 8 until you can go no further

Learn the numbers that add up to make 100.

e.g. 78 + 22
77 + 23
76 + 24

CHECK IT OUT

1 Write down the answers to these.
   a 18 + 36   **b** 85 − 27   **c** 128 − 58

2 Thea has £4. Can she buy 3 books costing £1.25 each?

3 Find the next 3 times for this bus route.
   Route A
   every 13 minutes
   07:10
   07:23
   $\vdots$

4 Find the missing numbers in these flow charts.
   a $\square \longrightarrow \times 4 \longrightarrow + 5 \longrightarrow 33$
   b $40 \longrightarrow \div 8 \longrightarrow + 12 \longrightarrow \square$
   c $17 \longrightarrow \times 2 \longrightarrow + \square \longrightarrow 39$
   d $24 \longrightarrow \div \square \longrightarrow - 8 \longrightarrow 4$

5 Work these out without a calculator.
   a 400 + 800   **b** 1200 − 750   **c** 2950 − 1750

4.2 MULTIPLYING AND DIVIDING

JUST DO IT!

You can use a calculator.

1 Find 3 ways of making 36 by multiplying.

2 Find 3 ways of making 40 by multiplying.

3 Find 3 ways of making 75 by multiplying.

4 How many ways can you find of making 16 by multiplying?

5 How many ways can you find of making 29 by multiplying?

A

1 Work out the answers without using a calculator.

a 10×8	**f** 25×3	**k** 24×2	**p** 26×7
b 12×6	**g** 40×4	**l** 34×3	**q** 32×8
c 14×3	**h** 50×5	**m** 52×4	**r** 43×4
d 21×4	**i** 60×3	**n** 47×3	**s** 51×6
e 17×3	**j** 25×7	**o** 36×5	**t** 72×8

2 Choose pairs of numbers from the grid below that multiply to give these numbers. You can use a calculator.

60   270   120   800   85   48   144   66

	5		20	15	12
16		10			6
2	12		3	22	
100	27	8	4	17	

3 Work out the answers to these without using a calculator.

a $40 \div 5$	**f** $42 \div 7$	**k** $48 \div 6$	**p** $77 \div 11$
b $36 \div 6$	**g** $80 \div 20$	**l** $45 \div 5$	**q** $27 \div 3$
c $20 \div 4$	**h** $100 \div 10$	**m** $60 \div 4$	**r** $32 \div 8$
d $18 \div 6$	**i** $24 \div 6$	**n** $63 \div 9$	**s** $64 \div 8$
e $40 \div 10$	**j** $80 \div 8$	**o** $35 \div 5$	**t** $81 \div 9$

4 Choose pairs of numbers from the grid below that divide to give these numbers. You can use a calculator.

24   7   15
8   6   20   16   4

3		80	64	25	
	6		4		42
8		100		120	11
72	60	7	77		5

> **Division** is the **inverse** of **multiplication**.
> **Multiplication** is the **inverse** of **division**.
>
> FACT

W B **1** Fill in the missing numbers for each question.

a $24 \div 6 = \square$ $6 \times \square = 24$ $24 \div \square = 6$

b $42 \div 7 = \square$ $7 \times \square = 42$ $42 \div \square = 7$

c $\square \div 5 = \square$ $\square \times 5 = 40$ $40 \div \square = 5$

d $32 \div 8 = \square$ $\square \times 8 = 32$ $\square \div \square = 8$

e $81 \div \square = \square$ $9 \times \square = 81$ $81 \div \square = 9$

f $63 \div \square = \square$ $7 \times \square = 63$ $63 \div \square = 7$

2 Number walls have special properties.

To find the next number in these number walls you multiply the two numbers below it.

W Fill in these to find the number at the top of each number wall.

a
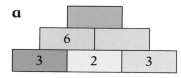

d
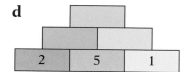

b
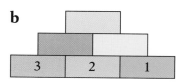

e
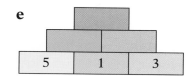

c
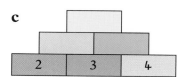

f
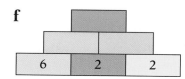

W

3 Find the missing numbers in these number walls.

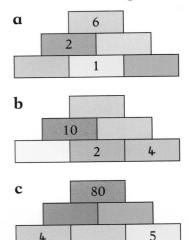

a

	6	
2		
	1	

b

10		
	2	4

c

	80	
4		5

d

	48	
	2	6

e

	36	
3		3

f

	27	
3	3	

C

1 Danni buys 4 cans of drink that cost 63 p each.
Terri buys 3 packets of biscuits that cost 89 p each.
Who has more change from £3?

2 Great Aunt Dollie leaves Sarah
and Pete the money for a year's
supply of strawberries. If the
strawberries cost £6.24 a month,
how much will they cost for
1 year?

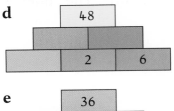
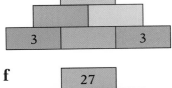

3 Kelly and Gemma are arranging a party.
They buy 18 boxes of crisps that cost
£4.75 each and 24 trays of drink cans that
cost £7.25 each.
a What is the total cost of the party?
b If 50 people come to the party, how much
should they charge each person so they
break even without making a profit?

4 Farmer Todd is fencing his paddock. The perimeter of the
paddock is 75 metres. The gate is 3 metres wide and each fence
panel is 2 metres wide. How many fence panels does he need?

5 Fiona is driving to her gran's house.
Her car does 15 miles per litre of fuel.
Her gran lives 90 miles away.

a How many litres of fuel will she use?

Her fuel tank holds 38 litres of fuel.

b How many miles could Fiona travel on
1 tank of fuel?

6   On a trip to a Theme Park 255 pupils were accompanied by
23 adults. The coaches held 49 people.
   a How many coaches were needed?
   b How many spare seats were there?

7   At Easter Mrs Jones gave her class of 28 pupils a jar containing
369 sweets.
   a How many sweets did they have each?
   b How many sweets were left over?
   c What should Mrs Jones do with the left-over sweets?

JUST DO IT!

Find possible missing numbers in these puzzles.

1

$$
\begin{array}{r}
\square\ \square \\
\times\quad \square \\
\hline
2\ \ 1\ \ 2 \\
\hline
\end{array}
$$

2

$$
\begin{array}{r}
\square\ \square \\
\times\quad \square \\
\hline
1\ \ 1\ \ 6 \\
\hline
\end{array}
$$

REVISION

FACT

Division is the **inverse** of **multiplication**.
Multiplication is the **inverse** of **division**.

LEARNING TIPS

Work answers out in your head first and then check your answer with a calculator

Look for multiplication and division patterns in the times tables

Multiplication and division questions can be answered using addition and subtraction (see Level 3!)

CHECK IT OUT

1 Fill in the missing numbers.

a $30 \times 4 = \square$

c $65 \div 5 = \square$

b $27 \times 3 = \square$

d $120 \div \square = 15$

2 Find the missing numbers in this number wall.
To find a number, multiply the two numbers below it.

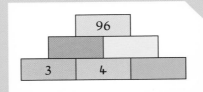

3 Mrs Davies is buying wall lights for her house.
She needs 40 lights. They cost £13 each.
What is the total cost?

4 Old Peter Grimm left £6000 to be shared equally between his seven grandchildren.
a How much do they get each?
b How much is left over?

4.3 MULTIPLES, FACTORS AND PRIMES

FACT

> 20, 40 and 80 are **multiples** of 10 because 10 divides into each number without a remainder.

You can use a calculator for these questions.

A

1 Which of these numbers are multiples of 10?
  a 9, 20, 26, 40, 60, 52, 45
  b 30, 18, 50, 82, 90, 15
  c 33, 60, 72, 100, 120, 97, 80
  d 10, 20, 18, 50, 22, 90, 53, 60

2 Which of these numbers are multiples of 3?
  a 20, 18, 14, 12, 15, 21, 27
  b 16, 15, 9, 3, 33, 35, 40
  c 19, 27, 18, 36, 24, 22, 12
  d 22, 24, 26, 28, 30, 32, 34

3 Which of these numbers are multiples of 6?
  a 6, 16, 26, 36, 46, 56, 66
  b 11, 24, 42, 60, 37, 48, 54
  c 40, 36, 55, 48, 72, 60
  d 30, 24, 12, 17, 28, 36, 7

4 Which of these numbers are multiples of 4?
  a 20, 18, 28, 38, 25, 24, 15
  b 34, 4, 64, 94, 14, 44, 104
  c 17, 16, 52, 8, 61, 40, 32
  d 32, 56, 24, 20, 80, 16, 88

JUST DO IT!

12 is a multiple of 2 and 6. It is also a multiple of 3 and 4.

Work out all the possible numbers that each of these numbers are multiples of.

27   36   40   100

A **factor** is a number that divides into another number without a remainder.

Example: 3 is a factor of 6.

TALKING POINT

Factors and multiples are connected.

3 is a factor of 6. 6 is a multiple of 3.

How can you remember which is which?

Peter used this sentence to help him remember:

   "You multiply to get a multiple."

Think of your own sentences for multiples and factors.

B **1** Find the missing factors for each number.

   a Factors of 6   1, 2, ☐, 6
   b Factors of 8   1, ☐, ☐, 8
   c Factors of 9   1, ☐, 9
   d Factors of 15   1, ☐, ☐, 15
   e Factors of 20   1, ☐, 4, ☐, 10, ☐
   f Which number is always a factor?

2 Find all the factors of these numbers.
   a 18   **c** 12   **e** 30
   b 22   **d** 25   **f** 50

3 **a** Write down the factors of 6.
   b Write down the factors of 8.
   c Write down the numbers that are factors of 6 and 8.

4 Find the factors, if any, that are shared by both numbers.
   a 8 and 10   **c** 14 and 24   **e** 12 and 26
   b 16 and 20   **d** 11 and 22   **f** 15 and 24

A **prime number** has only two factors, 1 and the number itself.

Example: The factors of 7 are 1 and 7.
          7 is a prime number.

JUST DO IT!

Use a calculator.

1 Put 17 into the calculator.
Divide by 2.
Write down the answer.

2 Put 17 into the calculator.
Divide by 3.
Write down the answer.

17 ÷ by	Calculator answer
2	8.5
3	5.6666666...
⋮	

3 Keep going until you get to 16.

4 Are there any whole numbers in the
answer column?
If the answer is no then 17 is a prime number.
Result: 17 is a prime number.

 1 Use a calculator to find out which of these numbers are
prime numbers.

a 5　　　　　　**b** 9　　　　　　**c** 11　　　　　　**d** 7

2

1	2	3	4	5	6	7	8	9	10
11	12	13	14	15	16	17	18	19	20
21	22	23	24	25	26	27	28	29	30
31	32	33	34	35	36	37	38	39	40
41	42	43	44	45	46	47	48	49	50

a Colour in all the prime numbers.

b Is there a pattern to the prime numbers?

3 Can a prime number also be a multiple? Explain your answer.

4 Can a multiple also be a factor? Explain your answer.

5 Can a factor also be a prime number? Explain your answer.

REVISION

FACT

20, 40 and 80 are **multiples** of 10 because 10 divides into each number without a remainder.

A **prime number** has only two factors, 1 and the number itself.

LEARNING TIPS

Every number is a special number. Check every number to see if it is a prime, a factor or a multiple

There is no pattern to the primes – you have to learn which numbers do not appear in the multiplication tables

Most factors come in pairs – but not for square numbers

$$4 - 1, 2, 4$$

does not have a pair

$$6 - 1, 2, 3, 6$$

2 pairs

CHECK IT OUT

1 Which of these numbers are multiples of 6?

9, 12, 15, 24, 30, 33

2 Write down the factors of 14 and 21.

3 Which of these numbers are prime numbers?

2, 4, 5, 9, 11, 21

4.4 DECIMALS

0.1 is **one-tenth** of 1.

A

1 Write these decimals in order, smallest first.
   a 0.4, 0.1, 0.2, 0.7
   b 0.3, 0.8, 0.9, 0.5
   c 0.5, 0.6, 0.1, 0.4
   d 0.9, 0.2, 0.7, 0.8, 0.4
   e 0.8, 0.3, 0.4, 0.1, 0.9
   f 0.6, 0.2, 0.9, 0.8, 0.3

2 **a** How many tenths is 0.4?
   b How many tenths is 0.6?
   c How many tenths is 0.3?
   d How many tenths is 0.8?
   e How many tenths is 0.5?

JUST DO IT!

Find out what happens when you multiply a number by 0.1.

Write a sentence explaining what happens to a number when you multiply by 0.1.

3 Add these decimals.
   a 0.4 + 0.5
   b 0.2 + 0.6
   c 0.8 + 0.1
   d 0.3 + 0.3
   e 0.4 + 0.3 + 0.2
   f 1.2 + 0.3
   g 1.5 + 0.4
   h 2.3 + 0.1
   i 3.4 + 1.4
   j 4.6 + 3.2

TALKING POINT

Joanna has made a mistake:

1.4 + 0.7 = 1.11   ✗

Add 1.4 and 0.7 on a calculator to find the correct answer.

Explain what Joanna did wrong.

4 Add these decimals without a calculator.
   a 0.2 + 0.9
   b 0.4 + 0.7
   c 0.8 + 0.8
   d 0.3 + 0.9
   e 1.5 + 0.6
   f 1.2 + 2.9
   g 3.5 + 0.6
   h 2.6 + 4.5
   i 3.7 + 2.5
   j 2.6 + 2.6

5 Write these decimals in order, smallest first.
   a 1.2, 1.5, 1.3, 0.8, 1.6
   b 2.4, 0.8, 1.5, 1.7, 2.1
   c 0.3, 1.7, 0.1, 1.2, 2.1
   d 6.3, 4.1, 5.2, 3.7, 1.9
   e 2.6, 8.2, 8.8, 5.6, 4.3
   f 6.8, 8.4, 3.2, 0.8, 1.5

JUST DO IT!

Carry out some research into decimals.

1 What does the word 'decimal' mean?

2 Who 'invented' the decimal point?

3 Find at least 3 places where decimals are used in real life.

4 Write a research report that includes everything you found out.

B 1 Subtract these decimals.
      a 0.8 − 0.4
      b 0.9 − 0.7
      c 0.4 − 0.1
      d 0.9 − 0.3
      e 0.7 − 0.3
      f 1.0 − 0.4
      g 0.6 − 0.2
      h 0.8 − 0.5
      i 1.0 − 0.8
      j 1.0 − 0.3

TALKING POINT

Aaron has made a mistake:

5.1 − 0.4 = 1.1   ✗

Subtract 0.4 from 5.1 on a calculator to find the correct answer.

Explain what Aaron did wrong.

2   Subtract these decimals without a calculator.

a 2.7 − 1.1   **f** 3.4 − 1.5
b 3.8 − 2.4   **g** 5.5 − 2.8
c 6.5 − 1.3   **h** 1.2 − 0.8
d 8.9 − 5.4   **i** 2.3 − 1.9
e 7.8 − 4.4   **j** 8.1 − 7.4

3   Write down which decimal calculation gives the largest answer.

a 1.4 + 2.8 or 4.4 − 0.1   **f** 0.4 + 1.7 + 0.2 or 8.7 − 2.6
b 0.8 + 2.7 or 8.9 − 4.4   **g** 0.8 + 0.3 + 0.5 or 6.8 − 5.8
c 1.5 + 1.8 or 7.5 − 5.0   **h** 1.1 + 2.1 + 3.1 or 9.1 − 3.1
d 0.6 + 0.7 or 6.4 − 4.9   **i** 9.8 + 1.4 or 20.0 − 3.7
e 2.7 + 1.8 or 10.0 − 2.5   **j** 7.5 + 17.5 or 28.4 − 4.8

TALKING POINT

0.4 is larger than 0.08

0.4 > 0.08

Although 4 is a smaller number than 8 when they are both in the units column, in these numbers 4 is in the tenths column and 8 is in the hundredths column.

You can see this more clearly if you write one number under the other with the decimal points lined up:

units	.	$\frac{1}{10}$	$\frac{1}{100}$
0	.	4	
0	.	0	8

Sam made up this rule to help him remember:

"The further away the number is from the decimal point the smaller it is."

Is Sam's rule correct?
Does it always work?

C **1** Which number is smaller?
  a 0.4 or 0.04
  b 0.3 or 0.08
  c 0.7 or 0.01
  d 0.21 or 0.5
  e 0.72 or 0.8
  f 0.54 or 0.45
  g 0.312 or 0.5
  h 0.015 or 0.04
  i 0.601 or 0.7
  j 0.0021 or 0.01

2 Write these numbers in order, smallest first.
  a 0.2, 0.8, 0.7, 0.3, 0.4
  b 0.21, 0.05, 0.18, 0.34
  c 0.04, 0.012, 0.42, 0.36
  d 0.225, 0.182, 0.072, 0.055
  e 0.701, 0.062, 0.41, 0.318, 0.24
  f 0.66, 0.412, 0.099, 0.44, 0.7

3 **a** Daryl has measured the height of the people in his class.
    Write the heights in order, shortest first.

    1.41 m   1.52 m   1.63 m   1.51 m   1.7 m
    1.62 m   1.72 m   1.58 m   1.65 m   1.61 m

  b What is the difference in height between the tallest and the
    shortest person?

4 **a** Joe has measured the height of the people in his class.
    Write the heights in order, shortest first.

    1.53 m   1.49 m   1.61 m   1.51 m   1.52 m
    1.64 m   1.62 m   1.74 m   1.49 m

  b What is the difference in height between the tallest and the
    shortest person?

  c What is the height of the middle person?

REVISION

0.1 is **one-tenth** of 1.

LEARNING TIPS

Draw a decimal number ladder and fill in the missing numbers

0.4

0.2

Make a Place Value Grid

units . $\frac{1}{10}$ $\frac{1}{100}$ $\frac{1}{1000}$ $\frac{1}{10000}$

.

.

.

Write decimal numbers on the grid to find out which are larger or smaller

CHECK IT OUT

1 Write these numbers in order, smallest first.
   0.4, 1.4, 0.1, 0.9, 2.1

2 Add these decimals.
   a 0.5 + 0.3
   b 1.4 + 0.9

3 Subtract these decimals.
   a 1.0 − 0.6
   b 2.4 − 1.7

4 Write down the largest number in each pair.
   a 0.18 or 0.8
   b 0.401 or 0.32

5 Write these numbers in order, smallest first.
   0.315, 0.53, 0.153, 0.035

4.5 NUMBERS AND PLACE VALUE

The position of a digit determines its value.

Example: this 4 is worth four thousand   4000

this 4 is worth forty   1041

this 4 is worth four thousandths   0.004

Each column either side of the decimal point has a different value.

thousands	hundreds	tens	.	tenths	hundredths	thousandths
			.			

A

1 Write each number in words.

a 24	**d** 49	**g** 1359	**j** 6008
b 8	**e** 132	**h** 304	**k** 5104
c 93	**f** 984	**i** 7325	**l** 2098

2 Write down the value of the 3 in each of these numbers.

a 13	**d** 3150	**g** 6035	**j** 319.5
b 324	**e** 2359	**h** 7309	**k** 73.5
c 273	**f** 38	**i** 113.4	**l** 1326

3 Write down the value of the 7 in each of these numbers.

a 4.7	**d** 17.82	**g** 0.007	**j** 0.2172
b 14.07	**e** 175.63	**h** 15.172	**k** 11.75
c 29.7	**f** 200.57	**i** 517.3	**l** 10.071

JUST DO IT!

You need a 10-sided dice.

Draw 2 grids like this:

Roll the dice 5 times.

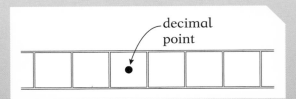

decimal point

1 Use the 5 digits to make the largest number you can. Write it down.

2 Rearrange the digits to make the smallest number you can. Write it down.

3 Find the difference between the 2 numbers.

4   Write these numbers in digit form.
   a fifty-six
   b one hundred and seventeen
   c two hundred and eleven
   d nine hundred and nine
   e seven thousand one hundred
   f two thousand and twenty-eight

JUST DO IT!

Shape Numbers

You need: squared paper and colours.

This is a 2 by 2 square.

It is made up of 4 squares
altogether.

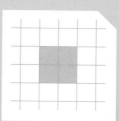

Draw more squares to answer these questions.

1 How many squares is a 3 by 3 square made from?

2 How many squares is a 4 by 4 square made from?

3 How many squares is a 5 by 5 square made from?

This is a triangle.

It is made from 6 squares.

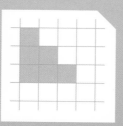

Draw some more triangles and
find out how many squares
they are made from.

Can you find a square number that is also a triangular number?

B   **1**   Copy and complete this square number table.

	1st	2nd	3rd	4th	5th	6th	7th	8th
square numbers	1	4						

2 Square numbers can be made by multiplying.
Copy and complete this table.

starting number	multiplication	square mumber
1	1×1	1
2	2×2	4
3	3×3	
4		
5		
6		
7		
8		

3 Copy and complete this triangular number table.

	1st	2nd	3rd	4th	5th	6th	7th	8th
triangle numbers								

4 Triangular numbers can be made by adding.
Copy and complete this table.

how many numbers	addition	triangular number
1	1	1
2	$1 + 2$	4
3	$1 + 2 + 3$	
4	$1 + \ldots$	
5		
6		
7		
8		

7^2 means seven squared.
$7^2 = 7 \times 7 = 49$

FACT

C   **1** Write down the value of each of these.
  a 2^2 **b** 8^2 **c** 6^2 **d** 5^2 **e** 10^2

  2 Write each number using squared notation.
  a 36   **b** 25   **c** 16   **d** 81   **e** 64

REVISION

FACT

The position of a digit determines its value.

Each column either side of the decimal point has a different value.

7^2 means seven **squared**.

LEARNING TIPS

Write numbers under each other to work out which is larger or smaller.

0.31   0.103

```
0 . 3 1
0 . 1 0 3
    ↑
```

Check tenths column first

To find square or triangular numbers use counters or scraps of paper to make squares or triangles

 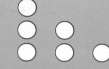

or

1×1	1
2×2	$1 + 2$
3×3 etc.	$1 + 2 + 3$ etc.

CHECK IT OUT

1   Write 6341 and 11 004 in words.

2   What is the value of the 4 in each number?
    a 0.41   **b** 43.02

3   Write these numbers in digit form.
    a four thousand and twenty-two
    b three hundred and thirty-nine

4   Which of these numbers are square numbers?
    2   4   8   15   16   24   25

5   What is the fifth triangular number?

4.6 THE FOUR OPERATIONS:
+ − × ÷

TALKING POINT

How many boxes do you need to pack 600 eggs? Each box takes 12.

How much does it cost for 12 people to go to a theme park at £27.50 each?

How much does Jason earn if he earns £200 a month less than Philip and Philip earns £632 a month?

> **FACT**
>
> There are 4 main **operations**: **add**, **subtract**, **multiply** and **divide**.
>
> + − × ÷

A For each question first decide whether to add, subtract, multiply or divide. Then work out the answer without a calculator.

1 Tessa buys an outfit.
Find the total cost.

T-shirt   £16.99

skirt   £42.99

boots   £59.99

2 Richard is shopping for a new CD. Each shop has a different price.

a How much cheaper is Virgon than Mega Music?

b Which should he buy? Explain your answer.

3 Josie and her 6 friends are going to
Waterworld for the day.
It costs £24.50 per person.

What is the total cost of the trip?

4 Auntie Mabel has left all her money
to Josh and his 2 brothers to be shared
equally between them.

Auntie Mabel has left £4300 altogether.

How much do they get each?
Explain your answer.

5 Sian and Stella go shopping for the same items in 2 different
supermarkets. Whose ingredients cost less and by how much?

	Sian	Stella
Chicken	£2.72	£2.68
Potatoes	89p	89p
Flour	42p	49p
Onions	13p	14p
Tea bags	£1.72	£1.68
Milk	52p	58p
Carrots	24p	22p
Margarine	53p	47p

6 Dave runs the tuck shop. Boxes of crisps cost £13.50.
How many boxes of crisps can Dave buy for £108?

TALKING POINT

What does £3.50 look like on a calculator?

Work out £10.00 ÷ 4 on your calculator.

The answer should be £2.50, not £2.5!

B **1** Use a calculator to find the answer to each calculation.
  a 4 × £2.50
  b £30 ÷ 4
  c £12.25 + £1.25
  d £60 ÷ 8
  e £27.35 − £13.25
  f £2 ÷ 20
  g 18 × £92
  h 42p + £18.38
  i 16 × £4.25
  j £500 ÷ 25

2   7   9   11   15   16   20   43   46

From the numbers above write down
  a 2 numbers that add up to 50
  b 2 numbers that add up to 36
  c 2 numbers with a difference of 7
  d 2 numbers with a difference of 9.

3 Find the missing length for each shape.

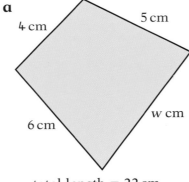

a

4 cm

5 cm

6 cm

w cm

total length = 22 cm

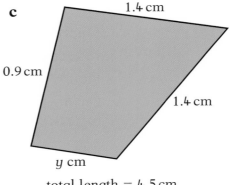

c

1.4 cm

0.9 cm

1.4 cm

y cm

total length = 4.5 cm

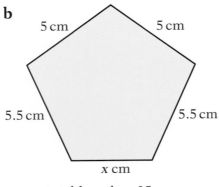

b

5 cm   5 cm

5.5 cm   5.5 cm

x cm

total length = 25 cm

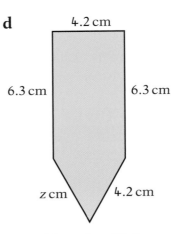

d

4.2 cm

6.3 cm   6.3 cm

z cm   4.2 cm

total length = 23.5 cm

1 Use a calculator to work out these problems.
Use the digits 1, 2, 3 and 4 to fill the boxes.

a

$$\begin{array}{r} \square\ \square \\ \times\quad \square\ \square \\ \hline 1\ \ 2\ \ 0\ \ 2 \\ \hline \end{array}$$

c

$$\begin{array}{r} \square\ \square\ \square \\ \times\qquad\ \square \\ \hline 4\ \ 0\ \ 8 \\ \hline \end{array}$$

b

$$\begin{array}{r} \square\ \square\ \square \\ \times\qquad\ \square \\ \hline 4\ \ 9\ \ 2 \\ \hline \end{array}$$

d

$$\begin{array}{r} \square\ \square\ \square \\ \times\qquad\ \square \\ \hline 8\ \ 2\ \ 6 \\ \hline \end{array}$$

2 Find the missing numbers in each calculation.

a
$$\begin{array}{r} 8\ \ 4 \\ 3\overline{)2\ \square\ 2} \end{array}$$

d
$$\begin{array}{r} \square\ 5\ \square\ 4 \\ 6\overline{)1\ 5\ \square\ 2\ \square} \end{array}$$

b
$$\begin{array}{r} \square\ 4\ 8 \\ 7\overline{)1\ 0\ \square\ 6} \end{array}$$

e
$$\begin{array}{r} 2\ 9\ 5 \\ \square\overline{)1\ 4\ 7\ 5} \end{array}$$

c
$$\begin{array}{r} 7\ 9\ 3 \\ \square\overline{)6\ 3\ 4\ 4} \end{array}$$

f
$$\begin{array}{r} 4\ \square\ 4 \\ 9\overline{)3\ \square\ 9\ \square} \end{array}$$

REVISION

FACT

There are 4 main **operations**: **add**, **subtract**, **multiply** and **divide**.

$$+ \quad - \quad \times \quad \div$$

LEARNING TIPS

Try and work out which operation you need to use before you start answering a question. You may need to use more than one

Practise different methods for multiplying and dividing. Remember you can use addition or subtraction to help multiply or divide

Don't mix units. Change everything to pounds or pence in this calculation:

£1.82 + 69p

or to cm or mm in this calculation:

4 cm + 28 mm

CHECK IT OUT

1   Justin buys 2 £1.99 magazines. How much do they cost and how much change does he get from £5?

2   Use a calculator to work out £13.27 − £4.17.

3   Find the missing length. Total length = 32 cm.

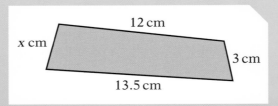

4   Find the missing number in this calculation.

$$\boxed{}\,)\overline{2\,9\,4}\quad^{4\ 2}$$

4.7　CO-ORDINATES

FACT

Co-ordinates come in pairs.
The first number is plotted **horizontally**.
The second number is plotted **vertically**.

Example: (2, 4)

W A　**1**　Plot each point on the grid on Co-ordinates Worksheet I.

a (3, 4)	**d** (4, 1)	**g** (0, 3)
b (1, 3)	**e** (5, 4)	**h** (1, 1)
c (2, 2)	**f** (3, 2)	**i** (2, 0)

W　**2**　Plot each point on the grid on Co-ordinates Worksheet II.

a (4, 6)	**d** (6, 1)	**g** (7, 7)
b (0, 8)	**e** (5, 6)	**h** (3, 0)
c (7, 4)	**f** (8, 8)	**i** (10, 9)

JUST DO IT!

Write down the 6 co-ordinate pairs on this line.

Explain the pattern.

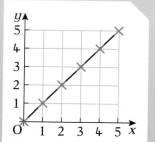

Write down the 6 co-ordinate pairs on this line.

Explain the pattern.

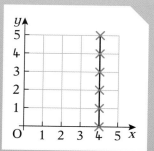

Write down the 6 co-ordinate pairs on this line.

Explain the pattern.

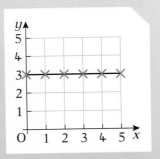

Write down the 3 co-ordinate pairs on this line.

Explain the pattern.

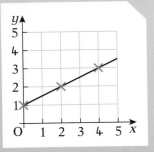

Draw some axes and lines of your own. Find the pattern for each line.

B

1 Nina has drawn the first side of a triangle. The line joins (2, 2) and (2, 8).

Write down 2 co-ordinate pairs that could make the third vertex of the triangle.

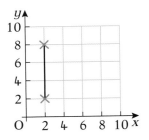

2 Adam has drawn 2 sides of a square.
   a Write down the 3 co-ordinate pairs that Adam has joined.
   b What are the co-ordinates of the fourth vertex of this square?

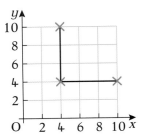

3 Colin has drawn 2 sides of a square.
   a Write down the 3 co-ordinate pairs that Colin has joined.
   b What are the co-ordinates of the fourth vertex of this square?

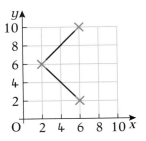

4 Laurie has drawn 2 sides of a rectangle.
  a How long are the sides of the rectangle?
  b What are the co-ordinates of the
     3 points already joined?
  c What are the co-ordinates of the
     fourth vertex of the rectangle?

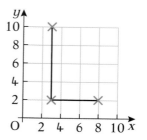

5 Hayley is drawing a kite on her
   co-ordinate grid. The points X and Y
   are opposite corners of Hayley's kite.
  a Write down the co-ordinates of X and Y.
  b Write down 2 co-ordinate pairs that
     could complete Hayley's kite.

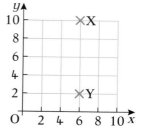

C Use the grid below to answer questions 1 to 6.

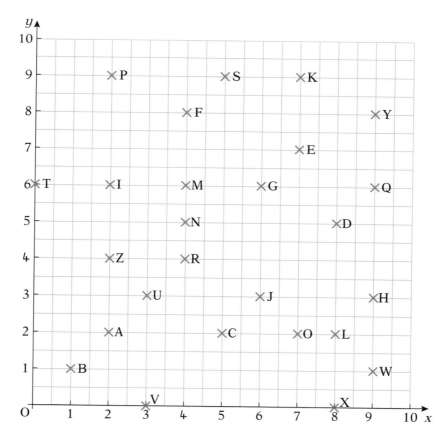

1 a Write down the co-ordinates for the word
     B U R G E R
  b Explain the co-ordinate pattern.

2 a Write down the co-ordinates for the word
C O L A

b Explain the pattern.

3 a Write down the co-ordinates for the word
P I Z Z A

b Explain the pattern.

4 KEY is a 3-letter word that makes a triangle if the co-ordinates are joined:

(7, 9)   (7, 7)   (9, 8)

a Find another 3-letter word and write down the co-ordinates.

b Find a 4-letter word and write down the co-ordinates.
What shape does it make if the co-ordinates are joined?

5 Work out these words by filling in the missing letters or co-ordinates.

a

letter		O			
co-ordinates	(4, 6)		(3, 3)	(5, 9)	(7, 7)

b

letter	V		T				
co-ordinates		(2, 6)		(2, 2)	(4, 6)	(2, 6)	(4, 5)	(5, 9)

c

letter		O				
co-ordinates	(9, 3)		(8, 2)	(2, 6)	(8, 5)	(2, 2)	(9, 8)

6 Write the alphabet in co-ordinates.

REVISION

Co-ordinates come in pairs. The first number is plotted **horizontally**. The second number is plotted **vertically**.

LEARNING TIPS

To remember to plot the points in the correct order, remember "*along* the corridor and *up* the stairs"

Look for patterns in co-ordinates and use the pattern to find other co-ordinates that have not been plotted

Divide up axes in equal amounts

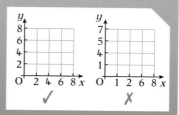

CHECK IT OUT

1 On squared paper plot these points:
   (0, 4)   (2, 3)

2 **a** Write down the co-ordinates of points A, B and C.

   b What is the pattern?

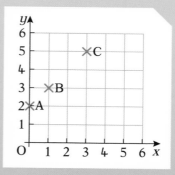

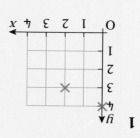

4.8 FRACTIONS

FACT

Multiply by the top number (**numerator**) and divide by the bottom number (**denominator**) to find the fraction of an amount.

Example: $\frac{2}{3}$ of £27

$$27 \times 2 \div 3 = 18$$

$$\frac{2}{3} \text{ of } 27 = £18$$

A

1 Use a calculator to find the fractions of these amounts.

a $\frac{2}{3}$ of £30   f $\frac{3}{4}$ of £12   k $\frac{4}{5}$ of £7

b $\frac{3}{4}$ of £40   g $\frac{1}{5}$ of £15   l $\frac{3}{4}$ of £18

c $\frac{2}{5}$ of £25   h $\frac{1}{4}$ of £10   m $\frac{3}{10}$ of £5

d $\frac{4}{5}$ of £20   i $\frac{3}{4}$ of £10   n $\frac{7}{10}$ of £20

e $\frac{2}{3}$ of £18   j $\frac{2}{5}$ of £8   o $\frac{6}{10}$ of £12

2 Find the fractions of these amounts without a calculator.

a $\frac{1}{4}$ of £8   f $\frac{3}{10}$ of £10   k $\frac{1}{4}$ of £2.80

b $\frac{3}{4}$ of £20   g $\frac{7}{10}$ of £20   l $\frac{3}{4}$ of £8.20

c $\frac{2}{5}$ of £15   h $\frac{9}{10}$ of £30   m $\frac{2}{5}$ of £12.50

d $\frac{4}{5}$ of £2.50   i $\frac{3}{4}$ of £2   n $\frac{7}{10}$ of £17

e $\frac{1}{10}$ of £30   j $\frac{2}{5}$ of £4   o $\frac{9}{10}$ of £15

TALKING POINT

What fraction of your time do you spend sleeping?

Mr Jones sleeps for 7 hours every night.

The fraction of time he spends sleeping is

$\frac{7}{24}$ ⟵ hours asleep
⟵ hours in the day

What fraction of your time do you spend doing each of these activities?

a eating   d singing
b homework   e visiting friends
c listening to music

What fraction of your time do you think you will use when you go to work?

B 1 Find the fraction of each person's time spent on each activity.

    a *Paul*

cooking	1 hour
eating	1 hour
shopping	2 hours
cleaning	2 hours
sleeping	8 hours

    b *Claire*

visiting friends	5 hours
sleeping	6 hours
working	7 hours
watching TV	2 hours

    c *Katie*

sleeping	12 hours
playing on computer	4 hours
eating	1 hour
talking to friends on phone	2 hours
watching TV	3 hours

    d *Daniel*

sleeping	8 hours
homework	4 hours
eating	1 hour
in the library	2 hours
working	7 hours
voluntary work	2 hours

2 Different people spend different amounts of their pay on food. Find the fraction for each person.

    a Mr Smith gets paid £220 per week. He spends £90 on food.
    b Mrs Peters gets paid £300 per week. She spends £70 on food.
    c Tony gets paid £80 per week. He spends £40 on food.
    d Justine gets paid £95 per week. She spends £35 on food.
    e Fiona gets paid £195 per week. She spends £52 on food.

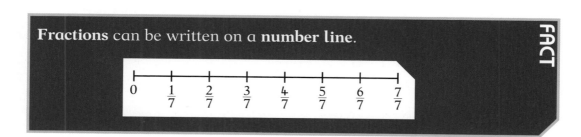

Fractions can be written on a **number line**.

FACT

235

W C Use the number lines on the Fractions Worksheet.

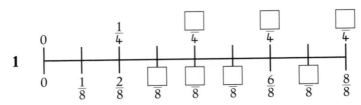

a Fill in the missing fractions.
b Write down the pairs of fractions that are at the same points
  on the line.

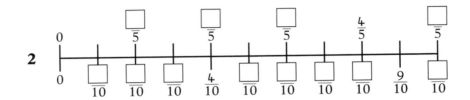

a Fill in the missing fractions.
b Write down the pairs of fractions that are at the same points
  on the line.

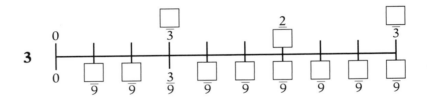

a Fill in the missing fractions.
b Write down the pairs of fractions that are at the same points
  on the line.

FACT

Fractions that are worth the same are called **equivalent
fractions**.

---

4 Choose 2 fractions that are equivalent fractions from each group
  of 3 fractions.

a $\frac{2}{8}$, $\frac{1}{5}$, $\frac{1}{4}$

b $\frac{3}{9}$, $\frac{1}{3}$, $\frac{2}{3}$

c $\frac{1}{5}$, $\frac{2}{10}$, $\frac{5}{10}$

d $\frac{2}{3}$, $\frac{6}{8}$, $\frac{3}{4}$

e $\frac{4}{5}$, $\frac{6}{10}$, $\frac{8}{10}$

f $\frac{2}{3}$, $\frac{4}{8}$, $\frac{6}{9}$

g $\frac{3}{4}$, $\frac{7}{8}$, $\frac{6}{8}$

h $\frac{5}{5}$, $\frac{3}{4}$, $\frac{3}{3}$

5 Write down these fractions in order, smallest first.

a $\frac{4}{8}$, $\frac{1}{3}$, $\frac{1}{4}$ **d** $\frac{4}{9}$, $\frac{9}{10}$, $\frac{4}{8}$

b $\frac{4}{10}$, $\frac{4}{5}$, $\frac{2}{5}$ **e** $\frac{3}{3}$, $\frac{3}{5}$, $\frac{3}{4}$, $\frac{3}{9}$

c $\frac{3}{9}$, $\frac{3}{4}$, $\frac{2}{3}$ **f** $\frac{2}{9}$, $\frac{1}{10}$, $\frac{3}{4}$, $\frac{5}{8}$

D Find the missing number in each calculation.

1 $\frac{1}{2} \times \square = 5$ **5** $\frac{3}{10} \times \square = 12$

2 $\square \times 30 = 15$ **6** $\frac{1}{4} \times \square = 4$

3 $\frac{3}{\square} \times 40 = 10$ **7** $\square \times 24 = 12$

4 $\frac{\square}{5} \times 25 = 10$ **8** $\frac{3}{4} \times \square = 30$

REVISION

FACT

Multiply by the top number (**numerator**) and divide by the bottom number (**denominator**) to find the fraction of an amount.

Fractions can be written on a number line.

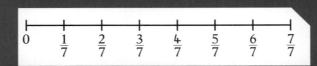

Fractions that are worth the same are called **equivalent fractions**.

LEARNING TIPS

The larger the denominator the smaller the single fraction. $\frac{1}{4}$ is smaller than $\frac{1}{3}$ even though 4 is larger than 3

Put fractions on a number line to help you work out equivalent fractions or which fraction is larger or smaller

Draw a rectangle and split it into fractions to work out equivalent fractions or which fraction is larger or smaller

CHECK IT OUT

1   Use a calculator to find the fraction of each amount.
    a $\frac{3}{4}$ of £20   **b** $\frac{9}{10}$ of £6.80

2   Richard earns £150 per week. He spends £50 on food.
    Write this as a fraction.

3   Choose 2 equivalent fractions from these 3 fractions.
    $\frac{6}{8}$, $\frac{3}{9}$, $\frac{3}{4}$

4   Write these fractions in order, smallest first.
    $\frac{3}{4}$, $\frac{1}{3}$, $\frac{3}{5}$

5   What is the missing number in this calculation?
    $\frac{3}{10} \times \boxed{} = 9$

4.9 PERCENTAGES

FACT

Percentage means **per hundred**.

TALKING POINT

10% of 20 is 2
10% of 16 is 1.6
10% of 120 is 12
10% of 4 is 0.4

Can you see the pattern when you find 10% of a number?

How would you explain the pattern to someone else?

Did you know that when you have taken 10% of a number you have 90% left?

What percentage do you always start with?

What percentage is left when you have taken 25% off?

SALE
10% off everthing!

A **1** Find 10% of each number

a 40	**f** 26	**k** 130	**p** 3
b 80	**g** 13	**l** 270	**q** 9
c 90	**h** 98	**m** 450	**r** 4
d 30	**i** 82	**n** 620	**s** 7
e 20	**j** 75	**o** 840	**t** 5

2 Find 10% of each amount.

a £30	**f** £28	**k** £260	**p** £2
b £20	**g** £36	**l** £370	**q** £4
c £70	**h** £92	**m** £650	**r** £7
d £90	**i** £84	**n** £740	**s** £5
e £50	**j** £18	**o** £910	**t** £8

3 Find 10% of each amount.

a 20 mm	**f** 32 m	**k** 120 m	**p** 2 cm
b 70 mm	**g** 15 m	**l** 350 m	**q** 8 cm
c 90 mm	**h** 65 m	**m** 480 m	**r** 7 cm
d 80 mm	**i** 82 m	**n** 720 m	**s** 4 cm
e 60 mm	**j** 77 m	**o** 810 m	**t** 6 cm

4   Find 10% of each amount.

a	20 kg	**f**	15 kg	**k**	360 g	**p**	1 kg
b	60 kg	**g**	95 kg	**l**	840 g	**q**	7 kg
c	50 kg	**h**	72 kg	**m**	770 g	**r**	8 kg
d	40 kg	**i**	66 kg	**n**	690 g	**s**	10 kg
e	90 kg	**j**	51 kg	**o**	290 g	**t**	3 kg

5   How much does each item cost in the sale?

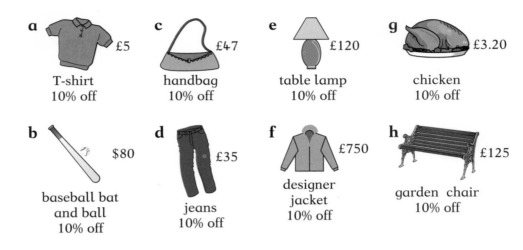

a T-shirt £5 — 10% off
c handbag £47 — 10% off
e table lamp £120 — 10% off
g chicken £3.20 — 10% off
b baseball bat and ball $80 — 10% off
d jeans £35 — 10% off
f designer jacket £750 — 10% off
h garden chair £125 — 10% off

6   Take 10% off each amount. Example: £50 − £5 = £45

a	£30	**f**	£150	**k**	£1.20	**p**	£50.40
b	£17	**g**	£128	**l**	£4.30	**q**	£27.30
c	£48	**h**	£212	**m**	£17.20	**r**	£15.20
d	£25	**i**	£162	**n**	£32.40	**s**	£40.20
e	£92	**j**	£840	**o**	£42.20	**t**	£49.80

VAT is a tax. The main rate of VAT is $17\frac{1}{2}\%$.
$17\frac{1}{2}\% = 10\% + 5\% + 2\frac{1}{2}\%$.

FACT

To find the VAT on an item find 10%, then 5%, then $2\frac{1}{2}\%$, and add them up.

Mr Patel sells TVs.

He wants to sell this TV for £200.

He adds on $17\frac{1}{2}\%$.

The buyer pays the total amount and
Mr Patel sends the tax to the Inland Revenue.

TV Shop
£200 + VAT

VAT   10% of £200   = £20
        5% of £200   = £10
        $2\frac{1}{2}\%$ of £200   = £5
        _____
        Total   £35

Retail price
£235

B **1** Find the VAT and retail price for each item.

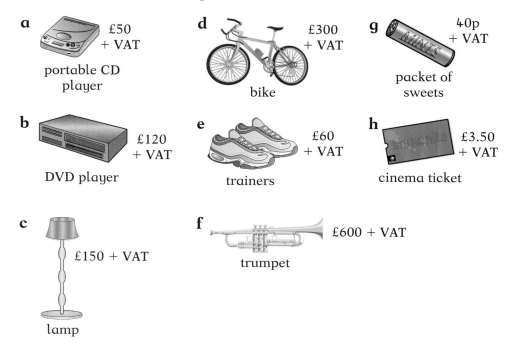

a £50 + VAT — portable CD player

b £120 + VAT — DVD player

c £150 + VAT — lamp

d £300 + VAT — bike

e £60 + VAT — trainers

f £600 + VAT — trumpet

g 40p + VAT — packet of sweets

h £3.50 + VAT — cinema ticket

2 Match the VAT to the price.

Price	VAT
£80	70p
£13	£4.38
£25	£17.50
£4	£14
£110	£2.28
£100	£19.25

JUST DO IT!

Income Tax

Different people pay different amounts of income tax depending upon how much they earn.

Write to the Inland Revenue or use the Internet to find out how much income tax these people pay:

Sally	**Luke**	**Deidre**	**Ali**
earns	earns	earns	earns
£12 500	£28 204	£42 750	£98 250
per annum	per annum	per annum	per annum

FACT

To change fractions to percentages follow this rule:
"Divide the top by the bottom and multiply by 100%."

$$\frac{4}{5} \qquad 4 \div 5 \times 100 = 80 \qquad \mathbf{80\%}$$

C **1** Change each fraction to a percentage.

a $\frac{3}{4}$ **c** $\frac{1}{4}$ **e** $\frac{1}{3}$ **g** $\frac{2}{5}$

b $\frac{1}{5}$ **d** $\frac{7}{10}$ **f** $\frac{4}{10}$ **h** $\frac{9}{10}$

2 Match the fractions to the percentages.

$\frac{3}{10}$ $\frac{3}{4}$ $\frac{8}{10}$ $\frac{1}{4}$ $\frac{1}{2}$ $\frac{7}{10}$ $\frac{1}{5}$ $\frac{2}{3}$ $\frac{6}{10}$ $\frac{2}{5}$

20%   50%   75%   80%   30%   60%   40%   70%   25%   67%

REVISION

FACT

Percentage means **per hundred**.

VAT is a tax. The main rate of VAT is $17\frac{1}{2}\%$.

$17\frac{1}{2}\% = 10\% + 5\% + 2\frac{1}{2}\%$.

To change fractions to percentages follow this rule:

"Divide the top by the bottom and multiply by 100%."

$$\frac{4}{5} \qquad 4 \div 5 \times 100 = 80 \qquad \textbf{80\%}$$

LEARNING TIPS

Use 10% as a base for finding other percentages. For 30% work out 3 lots of 10%

CHECK IT OUT

1 Find 10% of these.

   a 120   **b** 92   **c** 4

2 A £25 coat is reduced by 10%. Find the new price.

3 Find the VAT on a TV costing £140.

4 Change $\frac{2}{5}$ to a percentage.

4.10 NUMBER PATTERNS AND FORMULAE

TALKING POINT

These numbers increase by 2 each time:

3, 5, 7, 9, 11, ...

The pattern is: starting numbers, add 2.

These numbers increase by 2 each time.

4, 6, 8, 10, 12, ...

The pattern is: starting number 4, add 2.

What do the 2 sequences have in common?

What do each of these pairs of number sequences have in common?

A   5, 8, 11, 14, 17, ...
         10, 13, 16, 19, 22, ...

C   2, 4, 8, 16, 32, ...
         3, 6, 12, 24, 48, ...

B   7, 10, 13, 16, 19, ...
         7, 9, 11, 13, 15, ...

A

1   Write down the starting number, the pattern and the next two terms for each sequence.

a 5, 11, 17, 23, ...
b 3, 10, 17, 24, 31, ...
c 9, 13, 17, 21, ...
d 21, 27, 33, 39, 45, ...

e 50, 48, 46, 44, 42, ...
f 80, 75, 70, 65, 60, ...
g 27, 24, 21, 18, ...
h 40, 36, 32, 28, 24, ...

2   What do each pair of sequences have in common?

a 2, 4, 6, 8, ...
        2, 12, 22, 32, ...

b 40, 38, 36, 34, 32, ...
        28, 26, 24, 22, 20, ...

c 32, 35, 38, 41, 44, ...
        27, 30, 33, 34, 37, ...

d 80, 77, 74, 71, 68, ...
        24, 21, 18, 15, 12, ...

e 19, 17, 15, 13, 11, ...
        19, 22, 25, 28, 31, ...

f 36, 29, 22, 15, 8, ...
        56, 49, 42, 35, 28, ...

3 Greg has produced a number machine.

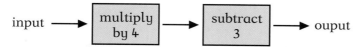

input → multiply by 4 → subtract 3 → ouput

When he inputs 3 the output is 9.
Copy this table and fill in the missing numbers.

Input	Output
2	☐
3	9
4	☐
5	☐
6	☐

4 Pia has produced a number machine.

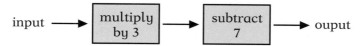

input → multiply by 3 → subtract 7 → ouput

When she inputs 3 the output is 2.
Copy this table and fill in the missing numbers.

Input	Output
3	2
5	☐
6	☐
☐	☐

5 Work out the numbers in the number machine for each table.

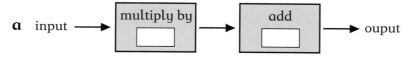

a input → multiply by ☐ → add ☐ → ouput

Input	Output
2	21
3	31
6	61
10	101

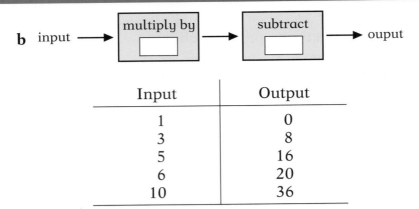

Input	Output
1	0
3	8
5	16
6	20
10	36

JUST DO IT!

You need: squared paper

1 Draw a square.
Write down the perimeter.

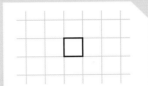

2 Draw 2 squares joined together.
Write down the perimeter.

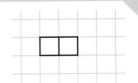

3 Draw 3 squares joined together in the same way.
Write down the perimeter.

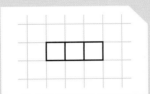

4 Draw 4, 5, 6, 7 and 8 squares each joined together in the same way.
Write down the perimeter of each shape.

5 Draw a table like this and fill in your results.

6 Copy and fill in the spaces to make this rule correct.

"Multiply the number of squares by _____ and add _____ to find the perimeter."

Square	Perimeter
1	6
2	
3	
4	
⋮	

7 Copy this flow chart and fill in the missing numbers to make it correct.

squares ⟶ | × __ | ⟶ | + __ | ⟶ perimeter

8 Copy this formula and fill in the missing numbers to make it correct.

$$\square\, s + \square = p$$

B Hugh's class has been finding patterns. For each question:
 a copy the sentence and fill in the spaces to make the rule correct
 b copy and fill in the missing numbers to make the flow chart correct
 c copy and fill in the missing numbers to make the formula correct.

1

Number of triangles	Perimeter
1	3
2	5
3	7
4	9
5	11
6	13

a Multiply the number of triangles by ____ and subtract ____ to find the perimeter.

b triangles → $\boxed{\times \underline{\ \ }}$ → $\boxed{- \underline{\ \ }}$ → perimeter

c $\boxed{}\, t - \boxed{} = p$

2

Number of hexagons	Perimeter
1	6
2	11
3	16
4	21
5	26
6	31

a Multiply the number of hexagons by ____ and _____ ____ to find the perimeter.

b hexagons → $\boxed{\times \underline{\ \ }}$ → $\boxed{\underline{\ \ }\ \underline{\ \ }}$ → perimeter

c $\boxed{}\, h \boxed{}\boxed{} = p$

3

Number of shapes	Perimeter
1	5
2	8
3	11
4	14
5	17
6	20

a Multiply the shape by ____ and add ____ to find the perimeter.

b shape → $\boxed{\times \underline{\ \ }}$ → $\boxed{+ \underline{\ \ }}$ → perimeter

c $\boxed{}\, s - \boxed{} = p$

4

Shape	Perimeter
1	10
2	14
3	18
4	22
5	26
6	30

a Multiply the shape by ____ and _____ ____ to find the perimeter.

b shape → $\boxed{\times \underline{\ \ }}$ → $\boxed{\underline{\ \ }\ \underline{\ \ }}$ → perimeter

c $\boxed{}\, s \boxed{}\boxed{} = p$

5

Shape	Perimeter
1	6
2	11
3	16
4	21
5	26
6	31

a _____ the shape by _____ and _____ _____ to find the perimeter.

b shape → 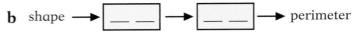 → perimeter

c ☐ s ☐ ☐ $= p$

Write a flow chart and a formula for each results table.

6

x	y
1	6
2	8
3	10
4	12
5	14
6	16

7

p	q
1	4
2	7
3	10
4	13
5	16
6	19

8

c	d
1	5
2	9
3	13
4	17
5	21
6	25

A formula for finding the perimeter of this rectangle is:

$p = 2l + 2w$

p stands for **perimeter**.

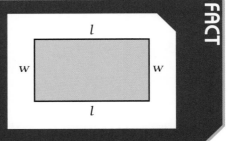

FACT

C **1** Write down the perimeter of each shape, e.g. $p =$ ☐.

a
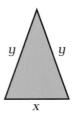

c
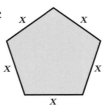

e
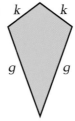

b
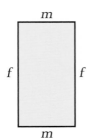

d
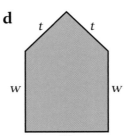

f
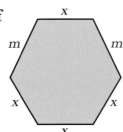

2 For each questions write down the cost of *x* cans.

a

b

c

3 For each question write down the cost of *y* packets.

a
24 p

b
32 p

c
98 p

REVISION

FACT

A formula for finding the perimeter of this rectangle is:

$p = 2l + 2w$

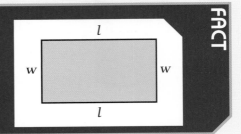

LEARNING TIPS

Count out loud. By speaking, your brain will learn more effectively:

"three", "five", "seven", etc.

Don't worry about using letters instead of numbers.
Remember $3x$ means $x + x + x$

Sequences can have the same pattern but different starting numbers

CHECK IT OUT

1 Write down the starting number, the pattern and the next two terms for each sequence.
  a 7, 10, 13, 16, 19, ...   **b** 50, 47, 44, 41, 38, ...

2 Fill in the missing numbers for this input/output machine.

Input	Output
5	☐
6	☐
☐	25
☐	33

3 Write a flow chart and formula for this results table.

x	y
1	6
2	10
3	14
4	18
5	22
6	26

4 Write down the cost of x packets of biscuits costing 48 p each.

4.11 LANGUAGE OF NUMBER

A **1** Copy the words and fill in the missing letters.
Choose from these letters.

M S V B I Y
E Q A P F N
U R D O

a _ U L T I _ L _
b _ I _ I D _
c _ U _ T _ _ C T
d _ _ _ C T I _ _
e _ _ U _ _ _ L _ _ T

2 Write down the meaning of each of these words.
  a percentage
  b inverse
  c place value
  d sequence
  e horizontal
  f vertex

3 Which letter has been missed out of all of these words.
Write the words with the letter replaced.
  a TNTH
  b DCIMAL
  c RCTANGL
  d PRIMTR
  e PRIM
  f HUNDRDTH

4 Rearrange the letters of each word to make a maths word.
  a FCAROT
  b DGITI
  c HTUOSNADHT
  d NMOEY
  e LIMCEDA
  f EVRTXE
  g HXAEOGN

W B   **1**   Play this game with a friend or partner.
Use the letters to make as many shape and space words as you
can. You can use each letter only once. The winner is the person
with the most words *and* the least letters left at the end.

O B I D V G R O A H U P P
N E A T E C A L N P E Q T
  X D C D A E A R N T S L
F E V N R G D O E I N M M
  A C O T E O T E P M R E V

PENTAGON

W   **2**   Use these letters to have another game.

A L E D A D I Y
B Q O P C M O L U
    A E S Y
E V F O E T D I
  G U M E N U H
O E T S I X L
  R I C H P
F T T M W
  M N

W   **3**   Use these letters to have a third game.

S A E L R T L I E
V H I R R
  E S S T E
A V I O G
Q E I Y S D T E
C C S T O V R
  O M D M X D p

4.12 SHAPES

W A   **1**   **a**   Match the shape to the name.

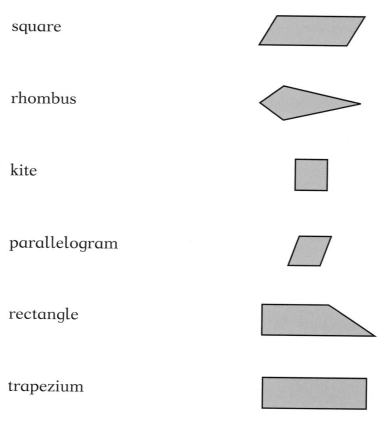

square

rhombus

kite

parallelogram

rectangle

trapezium

b   What do all these shapes have in common?

2   Write down the name of each shape from its description.

a   It has four equal sides.
The opposite angles are equal.

b   It has one pair of parallel sides.
It has four sides.

c   It has two pairs of equal sides.
It has four right angles.

d   It has two pairs of equal sides.
One pair of opposite angles are equal.

3   Write a description for each shape.
a   a square
b   a parallelogram

W **JUST DO IT!**

You need: a Shapes Description Worksheet
Work in pairs.

One person describes the first picture on
the worksheet.

The other person sits with their back to the
person with the picture.

They try and draw the picture
being described.

How close did you get?

Change places and use the second picture on
the worksheet.

W   4   Match the shape to the name.

isosceles triangle

hexagon

octagon   

equilateral triangle

pentagon

JUST DO IT!

Draw this triangle using a pencil, a ruler and pair of compasses.

side 1	side 2	side 3
5 cm	3 cm	5 cm

Draw one side of the triangle with a ruler and pencil.

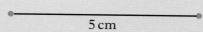

Open the compasses to the length of the next side (3 cm) and draw an arc from one end of the line.

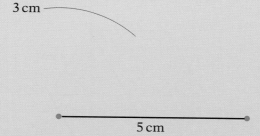

Open the compasses to the length of the last side (5 cm) and draw an arc from the other end of the line. It needs to cross the first arc.

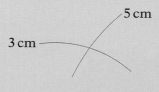

Join each end of the line to the point where the arcs cross.

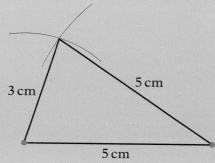

B **1** Draw each of these triangles accurately using a pencil, a ruler
       and a pair of compasses.
       a 4 cm, 5 cm, 5 cm   **c** 2.5 cm, 4 cm, 3 cm
       b 5 cm, 6 cm, 3 cm   **d** 7 cm, 4.5 cm, 6 cm

   2 Use the above method for drawing triangles to draw this picture
       accurately.

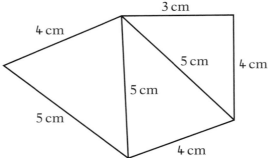

   3 **a** Draw this shape accurately using a pencil, a ruler and a pair
           of compasses.

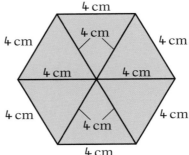

       b Draw this hexagon accurately using the same method.

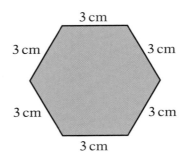

TALKING POINT

What is the difference between a two-dimensional (2D) shape and a
three-dimensional (3D) shape?

Which of these shapes are three dimensional?

      hexagon   cube   square   cylinder   tetrahedron

C   1   You need 1 cm square dotty paper for this question.

This is the net of a cuboid.   It makes up to this cuboid.

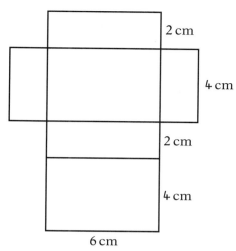

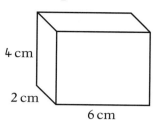

Draw an accurate net for each of these cuboids.

a

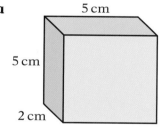

d

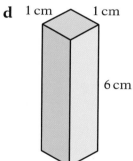

b

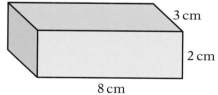

e

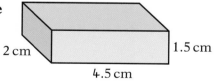

c

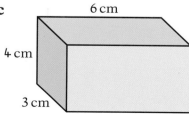

f

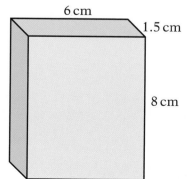

2 You need triangular dotty paper for this question.
Draw the cuboids that make up from these nets.
All of the lengths are in centimetres.

a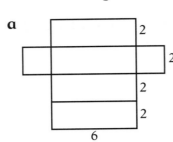

c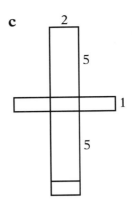

b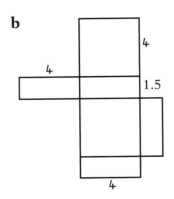

d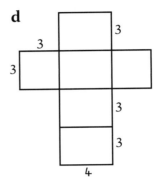

JUST DO IT!

This is a Mexican bean wrap, a delicious
lunchtime take-away meal.

Design a 3D box for this wrap.

Draw the net on square dotty paper.

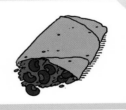

JUST DO IT!

Use 6 cubes to make different 3D shapes.
Draw each one on triangular dotty paper.

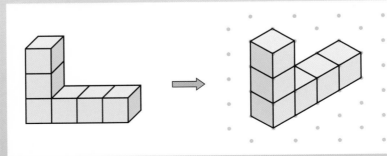

REVISION

LEARNING TIPS

Visualise unfolding a box to help you draw a net correctly

Hold your compasses at the top to help keep them open at the same measurement

Triangular dotty paper has 2 directions. Make sure you have it the right way round

CHECK IT OUT

1 Write down the names of these triangles.

a

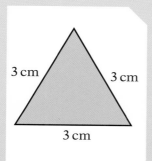

3 cm   3 cm

3 cm

b

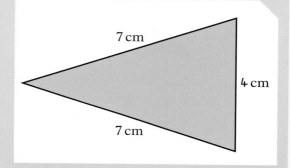

7 cm

4 cm

7 cm

2 What is the name of a six-sided shape?

3 Sketch the cuboid made from this net.

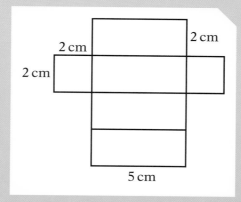

2 cm   2 cm

2 cm

5 cm

ANSWERS

1a equilateral **b** isosceles **2** hexagon **3**

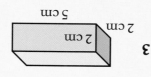

2 cm
2 cm
5 cm

4.13 SYMMETRY

FACT

This shape has **rotation symmetry order 3**.

It looks the same in 3 positions when it is turned.

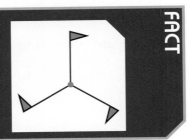

Different makes of car have a different logo.

A **1** Write down the order of rotational symmetry for each logo.

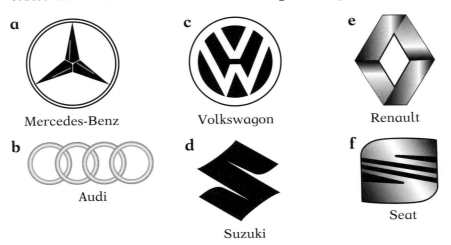

a Mercedes-Benz

b Audi

c Volkswagon

d Suzuki

e Renault

f Seat

2 Each shape has a section missing. Copy each shape and draw the missing parts to give the correct order of rotation symmetry.

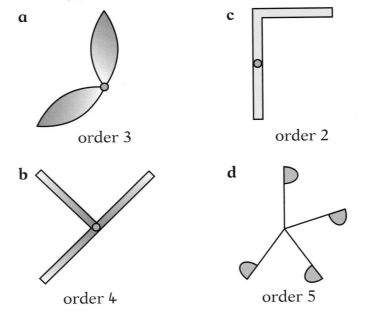

a order 3

b order 4

c order 2

d order 5

JUST DO IT!

Use a copy of the letterheading for your school.

Trace the school logo.

Use squared paper or a computer program to make an enlargement of your school logo.

If your logo is too complicated, choose another shape.

Squared paper method

Draw the logo.

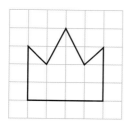

centimetre squared
paper

Draw the logo enlarged by scale factor 2.

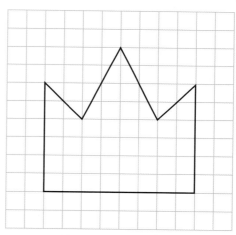

centimetre squared paper

Draw the logo enlarged by scale factor $\frac{1}{2}$.

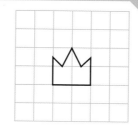

centimetre squared
paper

β 1 Enlarge each shape by the given scale factor of enlargement.
Use squared paper.

a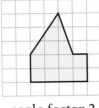

scale factor 3

c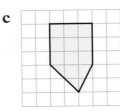

scale factor 4

e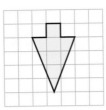

scale factor 2

b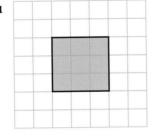

scale factor 2

d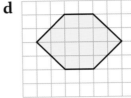

scale factor $\frac{1}{2}$

f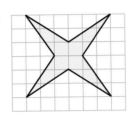

scale factor 3

2 What is the scale factor of enlargement for each shape?

a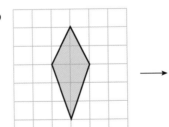

b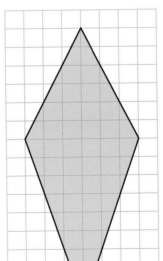

c

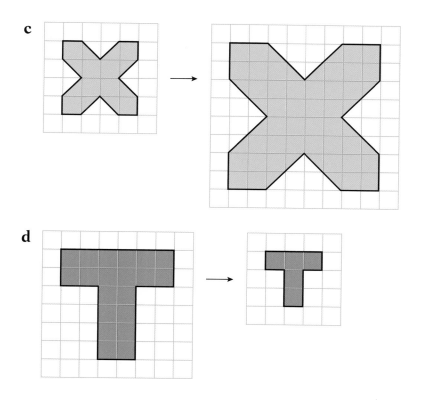

d

This shape has **translation symmetry**.

A shape stays the same when it is moved either horizontally or vertically, or both.

FACT

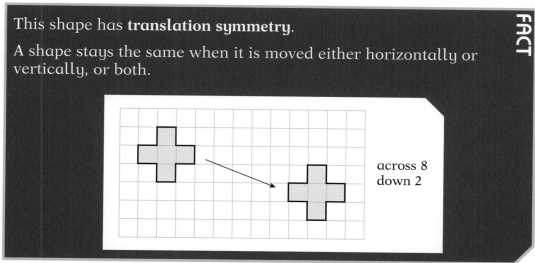

across 8
down 2

C Using squared paper, translate each shape by the given amounts.

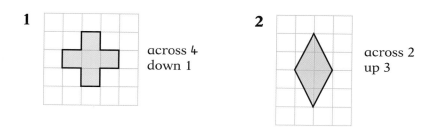

1 across 4
down 1

2 across 2
up 3

3 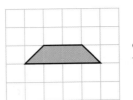 across 3
up 4

5 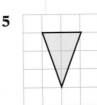 across 1
down 4

4 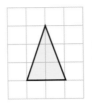 across 2
up 4

6 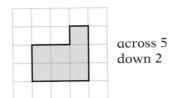 across 5
down 2

JUST DO IT!

Many of the border art designs in Microsoft Word or Publisher have translation symmetry like this one.

Find the distance between each pattern repeat.

Choose 5 or 6 patterns and find the distance between each repeat.

Make a display.

TALKING POINT

It is hard to see symmetry in 3D shapes.

Does a car have reflection symmetry?

Does a pair of scissors have reflection or rotation symmetry?

Does an umbrella have rotation symmetry?

Make a list of 3D objects that have reflection or rotation symmetry.

FACT

This shape has **rotation symmetry order 3**.

It looks the same in 3 positions when it is turned.

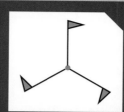

This shape has **translation symmetry**.

A shape stays the same when it is moved either horizontally or vertically, or both.

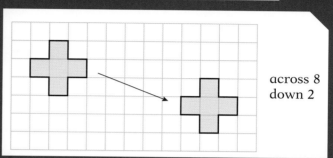

across 8
down 2

LEARNING TIPS

Some shapes have both reflection and rotation symmetry

Use a mirror to help you decide whether a pattern or shape has reflection symmetry

Use tracing paper to work out the order of rotation symmetry

CHECK IT OUT

1 What is the order of rotation symmetry of this logo?

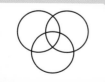

2 How many lines of symmetry does this shape have?

3 Enlarge this shape by scale factor ½.

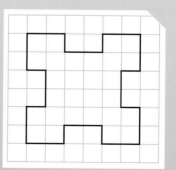

ANSWERS

1 3   2 6   3

265

4.14 REFLECTION

TALKING POINT

This picture of a face has reflection symmetry.

Did you know that no human face has reflection symmetry?

Some faces are more symmetrical than others.

How symmetrical is your face?

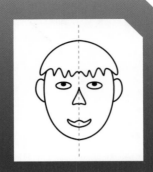

W A 1 Draw the line of reflection on each picture or shape.

a

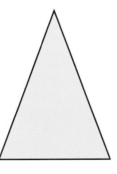

d

b

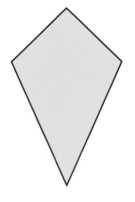

e

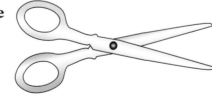

c

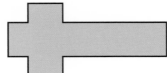

f

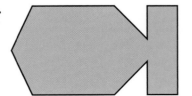

2 Draw the line of reflection on each shape.

a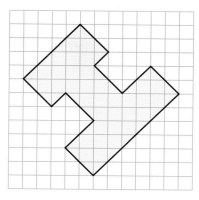

c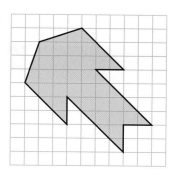

b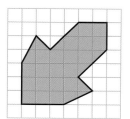

d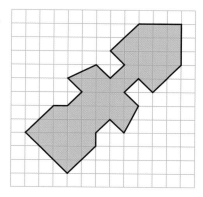

3 Complete these shapes so they have one line of reflection symmetry.

a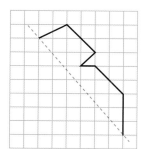

c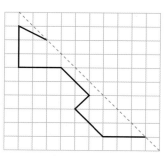

b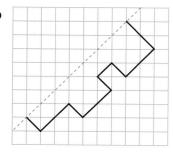

d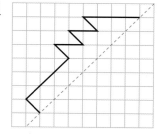

TALKING POINT

Some shapes have more than one line of reflection symmetry.

You can use tracing paper, a mirror, or fold your picture to find the lines of reflection.

W B

1 Draw the lines of reflection on these shapes.

a

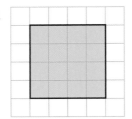

d

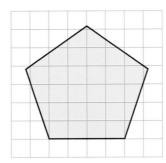

b

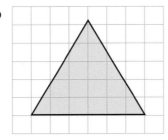

e

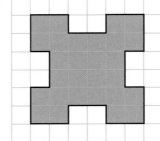

c

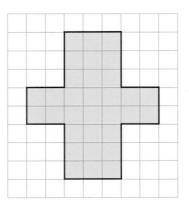

f

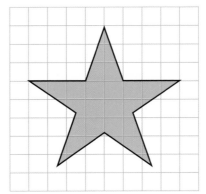

2 Complete each design to give reflection symmetry.

a

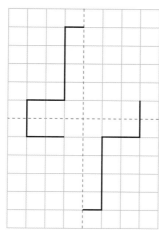

c

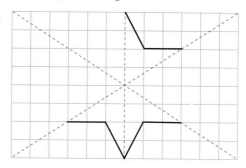

b

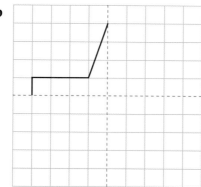

d

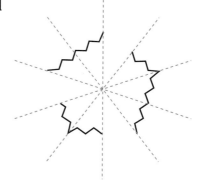

JUST DO IT!

The pattern on this mediaeval tile has reflection symmetry.

How many lines of symmetry does the design have?

You need: square paper

Research mediaeval tile designs. Design 3 different tiles based upon your research.

Choose your favourite.

Make a repeating pattern to show how the tile would look on a floor.

FACT

In **3 dimensions** shapes have a **plane of symmetry** rather than a line of symmetry.

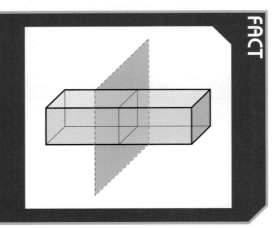

W C Draw the plane of symmetry on each shape.

1

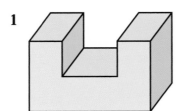

4

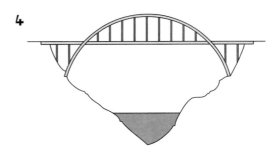

2

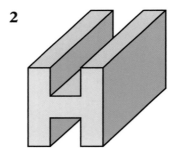

5

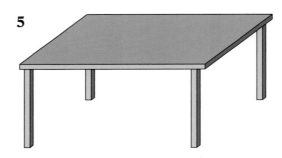

3

6

4.15 PERIMETER AND AREA

FACT

The **perimeter** is the outside edge of a shape or area.

A

1   Write down the length of the perimeter of each rectangle.

a

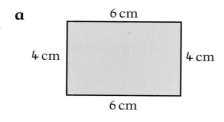
6 cm
4 cm   4 cm
6 cm

c

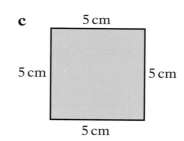
5 cm
5 cm   5 cm
5 cm

b

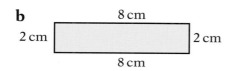
8 cm
2 cm   2 cm
8 cm

d

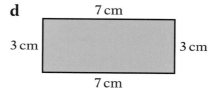
7 cm
3 cm   3 cm
7 cm

e   What does each shape have in common?

2   Write down the length of the perimeter of each shape.

a

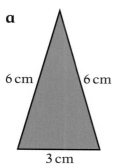
6 cm   6 cm
3 cm

c

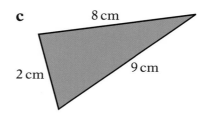
8 cm
2 cm   9 cm

b

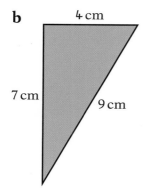
4 cm
7 cm
9 cm

d

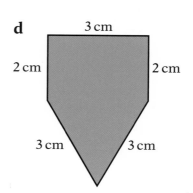
3 cm
2 cm   2 cm
3 cm   3 cm

271

e
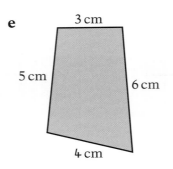

g
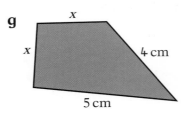

f
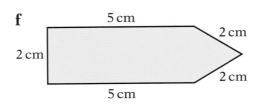

h
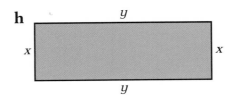

JUST DO IT!

You need: straws

1 Cut straws to these lengths:

3 cm, 4 cm, 5 cm

Use 3 straws to make this triangle.

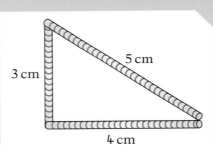

There are 2 other triangles you can make using any 3 straws.
Sketch them on paper.

2 Cut straws to these lengths:

2 cm, 3 cm, 4 cm, 4 cm, 5 cm, 6 cm

Use the straws to make as many different triangles as possible.
Sketch each one.

    5 triangles – Good
    8 triangles – Very Good
    10 or more triangles – Excellent!

3 Are there any choices that do not make triangles?
Explain your answer.

β **1** Find the perimeter of each shape.

a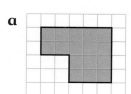

c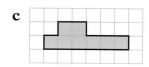

e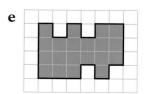

b

d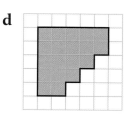

f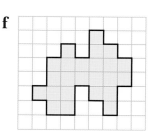

JUST DO IT!

You need: squared paper

This shape has a perimeter of 16.

Find and draw as many shapes as you can with a perimeter of 16.

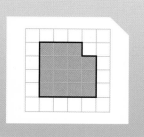

2 This swimming pool has a fence 1 metre from the edge.

How long is the fence?

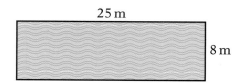

25 m

8 m

3 This picture frame is 30 cm wide and 45 cm long.

Find the perimeter of the frame.

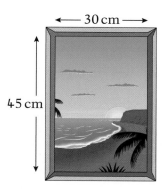

← 30 cm →

45 cm

JUST DO IT!

Walk around the perimeter of the school field.

Estimate the distance around the perimeter.

Measure the perimeter in metres.

How far out were you?

273

FACT

Area is often measured in **centimetres squared** or square centimetres (**cm²**).

C These shapes are drawn on centimetre squared paper.
Find the area of each shape in centimetres squared.

1

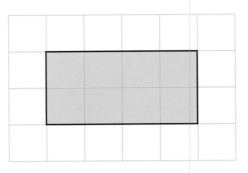

4

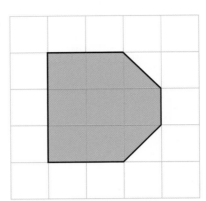

2

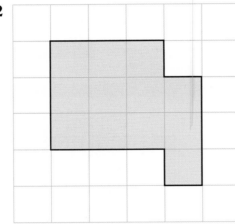

5

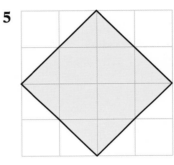

3

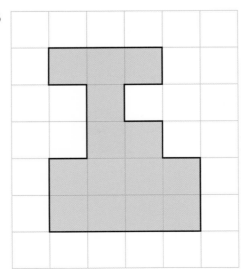

6

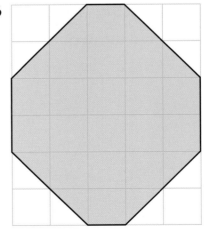

FACT

You can find some areas using **formulae**.

Triangle   area $\frac{1}{2} \times$ base $\times$ height $= \frac{1}{2}bh$

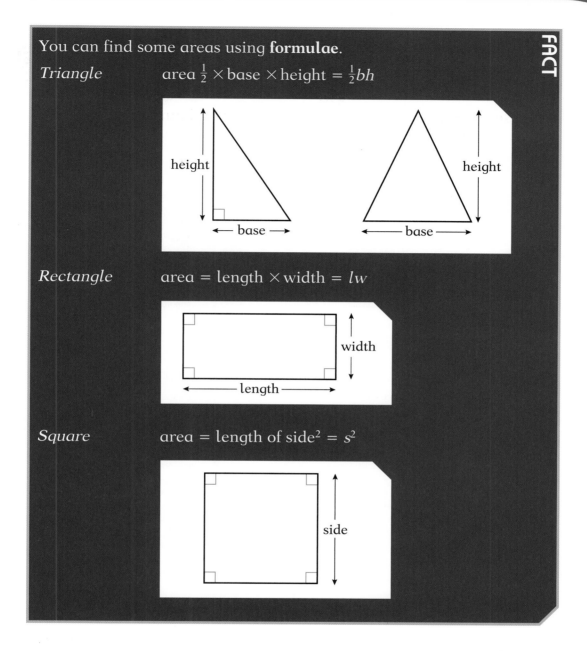

Rectangle   area = length $\times$ width $= lw$

Square   area = length of side^2 $= s^2$

D   **1**   Find the area of each triangle using the formula   area $= \frac{1}{2}bh$.

a

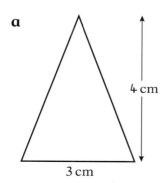

4 cm

3 cm

b

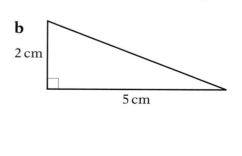

2 cm

5 cm

275

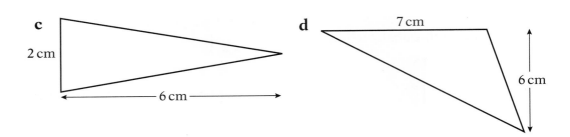

2 Find the area of each rectangle using the formula   area = lw.

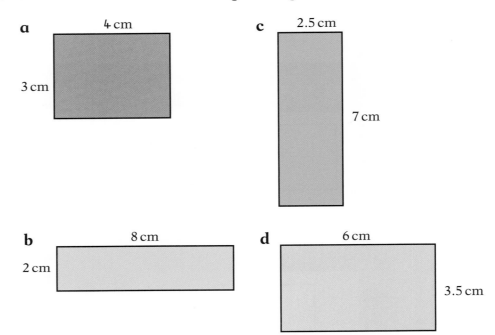

3 Find the area of each square using the formula   area = s^2.

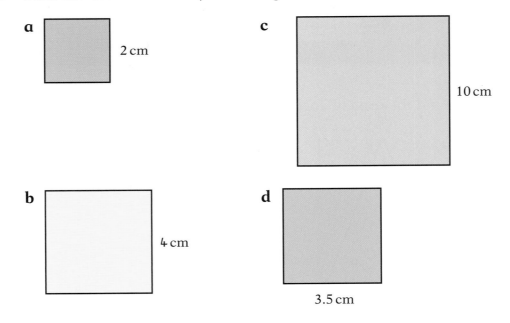

4 Find the area of each shape. Which shape has the smallest area in each question?

a

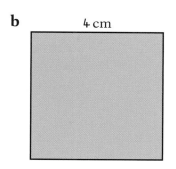 or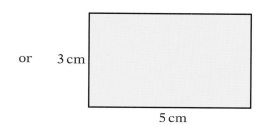

b

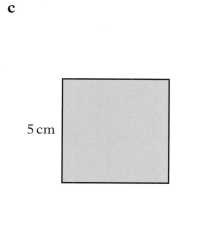 or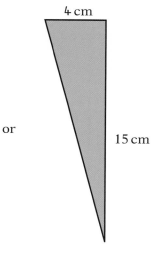

c

d

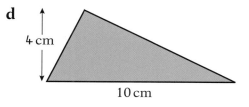 or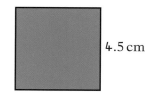

5 Write down whether these units are used for area or perimeter.

1 m², metres squared   **4** mm², millimetres squared
2 cm, centimetres   **5** inches
3 square miles   **6** feet

REVISION

The **perimeter** is the outside edge of a shape or area.

Area is often measured in **centimetres squared** or square centimetres (**cm²**).

You can find some areas using **formulae**.

Triangle area = $\frac{1}{2}bh$ *Rectangle* area = lw *Square* area = s^2

LEARNING TIPS

Remember that perimeter is round the outside – it has RIM in it:

peRIMeter

The height of this triangle is not 4 cm so this value cannot be used to find the area

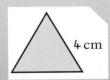

It is not true that a larger perimeter gives a larger area

CHECK IT OUT

1 Write down the area and perimeter of each shape.

a

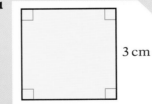

3 cm

b

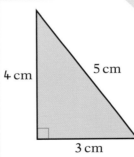

4 cm   5 cm

3 cm

c

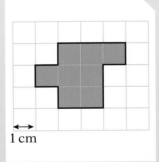

1 cm

2 Find the perimeter of this shape.

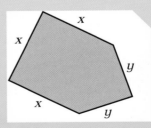

x x y x y

3 What is the formula for finding the area of a triangle?

4.16 ANGLES

FACT

An **angle** is a measurement of **turn between two lines**.
Angles are measured in **degrees** (°).

A **1** Measure these angles using a protractor.

a

c

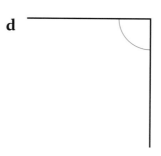

b

d

2 Which angle in question **1** is
    a a right angle   **c** obtuse
    b acute   **d** reflex?

Angles that join together at a point
add up to 360°.

$90° + 80° + 50° + 140° = 360°$

FACT

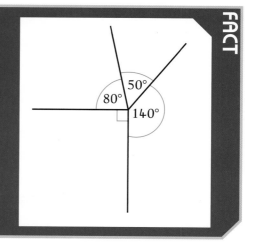

3 Calculate the angles marked with a letter.

a

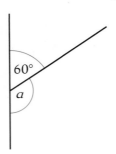

c

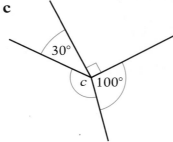

b

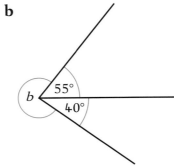

d

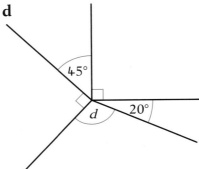

Angles that join together in a straight line add up to 180°.

20° + 90° + 70° = 180°

FACT

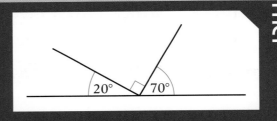

4 Calculate the angles marked with a letter.

a

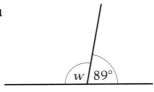

c

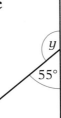

b

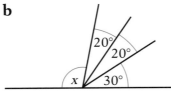

d

5 In each question, 4 out of 5 angles add up to a point.
Find the 4 angles.

   a 120°, 60°, 30°, 40°, 140°   **c** 170°, 160°, 150°, 10°, 20°
   b 75°, 100°, 25°, 200°, 35°   **d** 205°, 45°, 55°, 70°, 30°

6 In each question, 4 out of 5 angles add up to a straight line.
Find the 4 angles.

   a 70°, 70°, 60°, 20°, 20°   **c** 15°, 45°, 75°, 65°, 35°
   b 50°, 40°, 30°, 20°, 80°   **d** 15°, 110°, 100°, 40°, 15°

7 Use a ruler and protractor to draw angles.

   a 75°   **c** 205°   **e** 145°
   b 120°   **d** 30°   **f** 330°

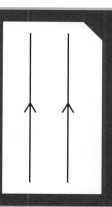

Parallel lines are lines that are always the same distance apart. They never meet.

The arrows show the lines are parallel.

When you cross parallel lines the angles have special properties.

FACT

ß **1** Which of these pairs of lines are parallel?

a

d

b

e

c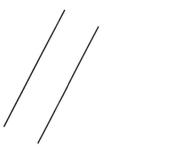

f

TALKING POINT

The opposite sides of a box of cereal
are parallel.

Think about all the other places you find
parallel lines or edges or sides.

How can you tell if two lines are perfectly
parallel?

How do you measure the distance between
two parallel lines?

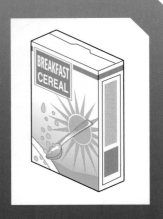

FACT

These two angles are equal.

They are called
complementary angles.

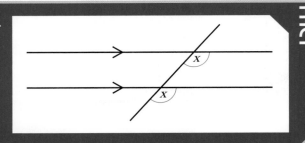

2 Find the missing angles in each question.

a

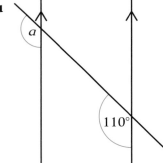

c

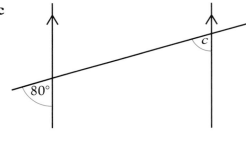

b

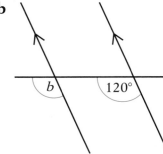

d

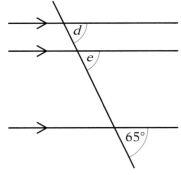

e

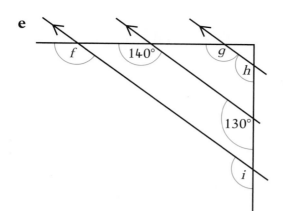

These two angles are equal.

They are called **alternate angles**.

FACT

3 Find the missing angles in each question.

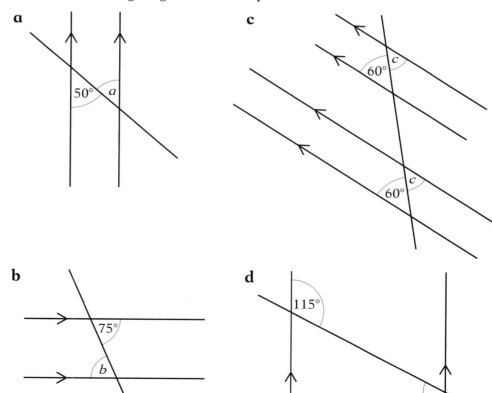

a

50° a

c

60° c

60° c

b

75°

b

d

115°

d

FACT

These two angles are equal.

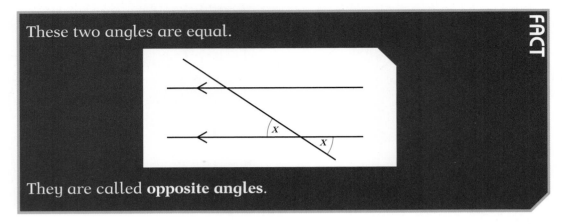

They are called **opposite angles**.

4   Find the missing angles in each question.

a

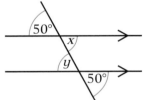

c

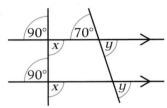

b

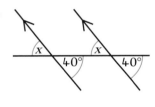

d

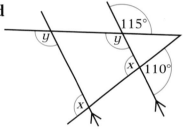

5   Use any of the angle facts to find these missing angles.
    For each angle write down the fact you used.

a

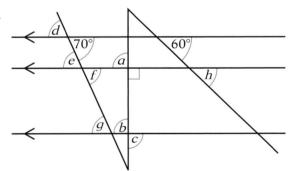

b

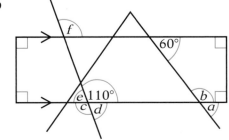

REVISION

FACT

An **angle** is a measurement of **turn between two lines**.

Angles are measured in **degrees**.

Angles that join together at a point add up to 360°.

Angles that join together in a straight line add up to 180°.

Parallel lines are lines that are always the same distance apart. They never meet.

These two angles are **complementary**. They are equal.

These two angles are **alternate**. They are equal.

These two angles are **opposite**. They are equal.

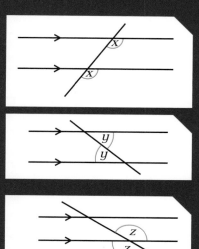

CHECK IT OUT

1 Which 4 of these angles would add up to a straight line?

   65°   25°   75°   35°   15°

2

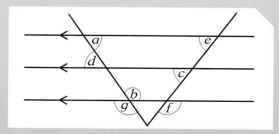

   a Which angle is equal to *a*?
   b Which angle is equal to *b*?
   c Which angle is equal to *c*?

4.17 READING MEASUREMENTS

A   **1**   Which numbers do the arrows point to on each number scale?

a

b

c

d

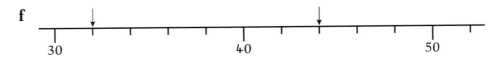

e

f

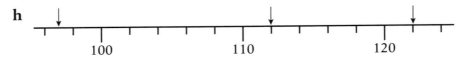

g

h

i

j

k

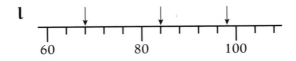

l

2 Which numbers do the arrows point to on each number scale?

a

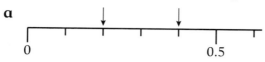

b

c

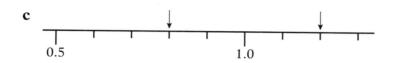

d

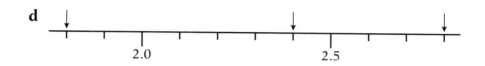

e

f

g

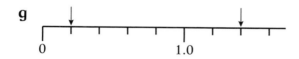

h

i

j

k

30.0   31.0

l

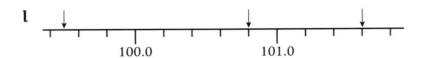

100.0   101.0

3   Which numbers do the arrows point to on each number scale?

a

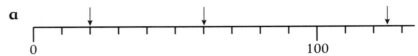

0   100

b

0   100   200

c

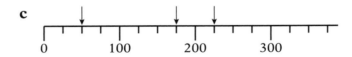

0   100   200   300

d

500   600

e

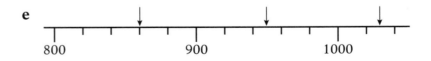

800   900   1000

f

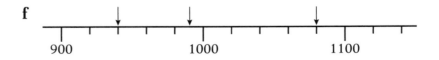

900   1000   1100

TALKING POINT

Where do you see number scales?

Number scales go up in regular amounts. How do *you* work out how much each mark on the scale is worth?

B **1** Read the temperature on each thermometer.

a

d

g

b

e

h

c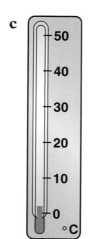

f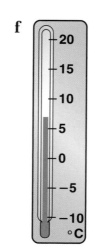

i

2 Petrol gauges in cars can look like this.

Each petrol tank holds a different amount of fuel.

The gauge shows this tank is full.

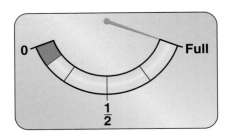

Use the scale and total capacity of each tank to work out how much fuel is left.

a

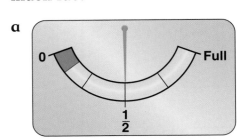

capacity 40 litres

b

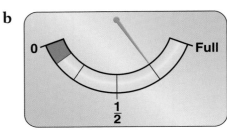

capacity 40 litres

c

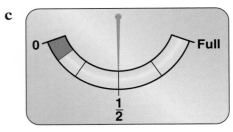

capacity 50 litres

d

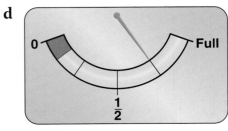

capacity 60 litres

e

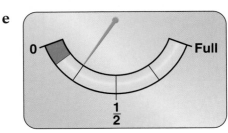

capacity 60 litres

f

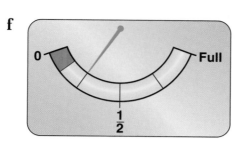

capacity 44 litres

g

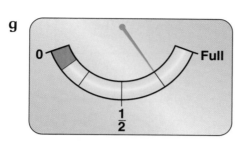

capacity 44 litres

g

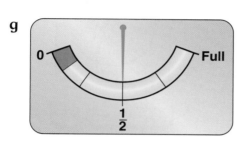

capacity 57 litres

JUST DO IT!

The weight of a BMW X5 3.0d is 2190 kg.
The fuel capacity is 20.5 gallons.

Find the weight and fuel capacity of other vehicles.

How would you convert gallons to litres?

3 Read the weight on each scale.

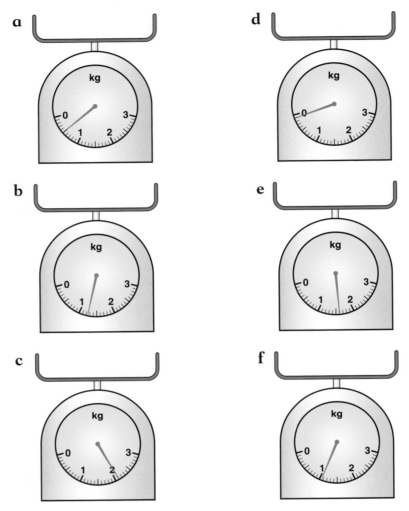

4 A conveyor belt automatically weighs bags of potatoes to make sure they are the correct weight.

Read the weight for each bag and work out how far it is from 5 kg.

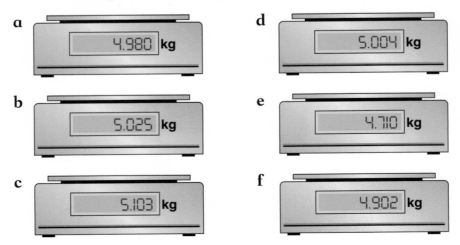

a 4.980 kg

b 5.025 kg

c 5.103 kg

d 5.004 kg

e 4.710 kg

f 4.902 kg

JUST DO IT!

Dog weight (kg)	Grams/Day
5	110
10	180
15	250
30	420
40	530
60	710

This table was found on a pack of dog food. It tells the dog owner how much food the dog should have depending upon how much the dog weighs.

If a dog weighs 15 kg it should have 250 grams of dog food.

How much dog food should each of these dogs have?

A

30 kg

B

2 kg

C

55 kg

Visit a supermarket.

Find other tables showing recommended amounts of dog foods or other products.

Write a report of your findings.

Do all dog foods recommend the same amounts?

REVISION

LEARNING TIPS

Make sure scales are set to zero before you start weighing

The best way to learn how to read scales is to practise weighing real items

Always check to see if your answer looks accurate. Number scales always go up in regular amounts

CHECK IT OUT

1 Which numbers do the arrows point to on these scales?

a
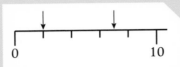

c

b
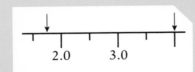

d

2 Read the temperature on each thermometer.

a
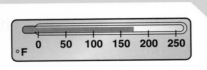

b

3 How heavy is this parcel?

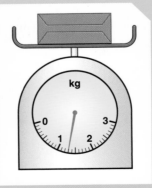

4.18 MEASURING ACCURATELY

TALKING POINT

How long are the white and yellow lines found on roads?
How accurate does the measurement have to be?

How much paracetamol is there in one tablet?
How accurate does the measurement have to be?

Talk about different measurements where accuracy is very important.

FACT

There are 10 millimetres in 1 centimetre.

$$10\,mm = 1\,cm$$

A

1 Change these measurements from centimetres to millimetres.

a 4 cm	**d** 19 cm	**g** 1.2 cm	**j** 26.4 cm
b 8 cm	**e** 27 cm	**h** 9.7 cm	**k** 30.9 cm
c 12 cm	**f** 38 cm	**i** 11.5 cm	**l** 98.2 cm

2 Change these measurements from millimetres to centimetres.

a 50 mm	**d** 380 mm	**g** 15 mm	**j** 362 mm
b 70 mm	**e** 420 mm	**h** 82 mm	**k** 406 mm
c 250 mm	**f** 730 mm	**i** 125 mm	**l** 713 mm

FACT

There are 100 centimetres in 1 metre.

$$100\,m = 1\,cm$$

---

3 Change these measurements from metres to centimetres.

a 3 m	**d** 18 m	**g** 2.4 m	**j** 12.25 m
b 8 m	**e** 32 m	**h** 6.8 m	**k** 40.8 m
c 12 m	**f** 57 m	**i** 15.2 m	**l** 19.98 m

4 Change these measurements from centimetres to metres.

a 240 cm	**d** 1830 cm	**g** 9241 cm	**j** 7120 cm
b 720 cm	**e** 4980 cm	**h** 1295 cm	**k** 2587 cm
c 825 cm	**f** 6200 cm	**i** 3080 cm	**l** 6008 cm

JUST DO IT!

Kitchen and bedroom furniture is measured in millimetres. A standard kitchen unit measures 600 mm wide.

Measure your kitchen and work out how many standard kitchen units would fit in.
How many gaps would you have?

FACT

There are 1000 metres in 1 kilometre.

$$1000\,m = 1\,km$$

5 Change these measurements from kilometres to metres.

a 2 km	**d** 20 km	**g** 3.5 km	**j** 10.68 km
b 7 km	**e** 32 km	**h** 7.2 km	**k** 3.824 km
c 11 km	**f** 75 km	**i** 9.82 km	**l** 20.042 km

6 Change these measurements from metres to kilometres.

a 4000 m	**d** 40 000 m	**g** 2700 m	**j** 19 820 m
b 9000 m	**e** 16 000 m	**h** 8500 m	**k** 27 385 m
c 15 000 m	**f** 82 000 m	**i** 11 280 m	**l** 60 204 m

7 The length of a football pitch is 95 metres.
   a Write 95 metres in centimetres.
   b Write 95 metres in kilometres.
   c Is the football pitch longer or shorter than 1 kilometre?

8 Five girls competed in the long jump at their school sports day.

Here are their results:

Adele	5.98 m
Susie	5.82 m
Sharon	6.13 m
Carys	6.04 m
Della	5.90 m

   a Who won the long jump?
   b Who came third in the long jump?
   c Write each jump in centimetres.
   d What is the difference in length between the winning jump and the jump that came second?

Find the long jump world record for men and the long jump world record for women and work out the difference between the two in centimetres.

In competitions the long jump is measured very accurately. To what degree of accuracy is it measured?

Find out your school's long jump records for boys and girls and work out the difference between them in centimetres.

9 The circumference of a circle is just over 3 times longer than the diameter.

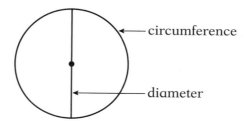

If the diameter of a circle is 120 cm, what is the length of the circumference?
Give your answer in metres.

Carry out research to find out about different measuring instruments and make a leaflet showing what each instrument measures.

Here are 2 to get you started.

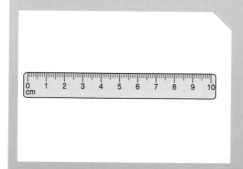

A ruler measures length in millimetres and centimetres.

A clock measures time in hours and minutes.

ß 1 Measure each line accurately in millimetres.

a _____

b _____

c _____

d _____

e _____

f _____

g _____

h _____

2 Measure each line accurately in centimetres.
Your answers will be decimal numbers.

a _____

b _____

c _____

d _____

e _____

f _____

g _____

h _____

3 Use a metre rule or tape to measure the length of the walls of
your classroom.

JUST DO IT!

Measure the height of everyone in your class.

Put them in order, shortest first.

Find the difference between the tallest person and the shortest person in centimetres and in metres.

FACT

There are 1000 grams in 1 kilogram.

$$1000\,g = 1kg$$

C

1 Change these weights from grams to kilograms
   a 3000 g   d 17 000 g   g 7200 g   j 12 909 g
   b 8000 g   e 29 000 g   h 12 500 g   k 10 002 g
   c 10 000 g   f 3500 g   i 4321 g   l 240 g

2 Change these weights from kilograms to grams.
   a 2 kg   d 72 kg   g 7.25 kg   j 0.275 kg
   b 5 kg   e 4.8 kg   h 10.38 kg   k 1.382 kg
   c 13 kg   f 12.5 kg   i 15.9 kg   l 0.004 kg

JUST DO IT!

Weigh everyone in your class in kilograms. Be as accurate as you can.

Look for the ideal weight for someone your height.

REVISION

There are 10 millimetres in 1 centimetre.

10 mm = 1 cm

There are 100 centimetres in 1 metre.

100 cm = 1 m

There are 1000 metres in 1 kilometre.

1000 m = 1 km

There are 1000 grams in 1 kilogram.

1000 g = 1kg

LEARNING TIPS

For lengths the pattern is

10 mm ⟶ cm

100 cm ⟶ m

1000 m ⟶ km

Always estimate your answer first. Does your pencil case really measure 32 metres?

1 pace is approximately 1 metre

CHECK IT OUT

1 Change each measurement to the given units.

   a 1.8 cm into mm   **e** 2.7 km into m

   b 250 mm into cm   **f** 10 200 m into km

   c 420 cm into m   **g** 5200 g into kg

   d 13 m into cm   **h** 1.384 kg into g

2 Measure these lines accurately in millimetres.

   a _____   **b** _____

4.19 THE LANGUAGE OF SHAPE, SPACE AND MEASURE

A **1** How many words can you find that have this word ending?

———————— AGON

2 How many words can you find that have this word ending?

———————— METRE

3 How many words can you find that have this word ending?

———————— THS

4 How many words can you find that have this word ending?

———————— ATION

B **1** Sort these words into words for lengths and words for weights.

metre   gram   inch

centimetre   pound

kilogram

kilometre   millimetre

2 Sort these words into symmetry words and angle words.

reflection   complementary

opposite   alternate

rotation   translation   enlargement

3 Write these words in alphabetical order.

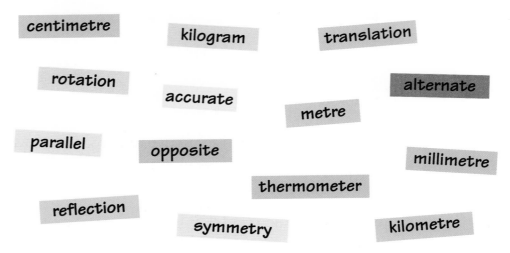

centimetre

kilogram

translation

rotation

accurate

alternate

metre

parallel

opposite

millimetre

thermometer

reflection

symmetry

kilometre

4 Write down the words that match these meanings.

a A type of symmetry. Something that has the same shape but is moved to another position.

b A measurement that is shorter than a metre but longer than a millimetre

c The symmetry that is like looking in a mirror.

d The word that describes two lines that never meet.

e The weight of a thousand grams.

f A five-sided shape.

g A four-sided shape with two pairs of equal sides and one pair of opposite angles equal.

h An eight-sided shape.

i A triangle with all three sides and angles equal.

j A measurement that is one-tenth of a centimetre.

4.20 COLLECTING DATA

TALKING POINT

Industries and organisations collect data.

Why does a TV station collect data?
Why does a medical researcher collect data?
Why do the police collect data?
Why do supermarkets collect data?
Why do football clubs collect data?

How do different industries and organisations collect data?

What data does your school collect and how do they use it?

Data you collect yourself is called **primary data**.

Data collected by other people, which you can find on the Internet, in tables and in reports, is called **secondary data**.

A 1 Use a Data Collection Sheet to collect this primary data from the people in your class.
   a shoe size
   b height
   c hand span
   d favourite TV programme
   e the last time they visited the dentist?

Use your data to answer these questions.

2 **a** Write the shoe sizes in order, smallest first.
   b What was the most common (modal) shoe size?
   c Who had the smallest shoes?
   d What was the range of shoe sizes?

3 **a** Write the heights of the people in your class in order, smallest first.
   b How tall was the tallest person?
   c Who had the middle (median) height?
   d What was the range of heights?

4 **a** Was the person with the smallest hand span also the shortest?
   b What was the largest hand span?
   c What was the total of all the hand spans?

5 **a** How many different favourite TV programmes were there?
   b Which was the most popular favourite TV programme?
   c Draw a pictogram to show the favourite TV programmes.

6 **a** Who had visited the dentist the most recently?
   b How many people had not visited the dentist for over a year?
   c How many people had visited the dentist in the last six months?

JUST DO IT!

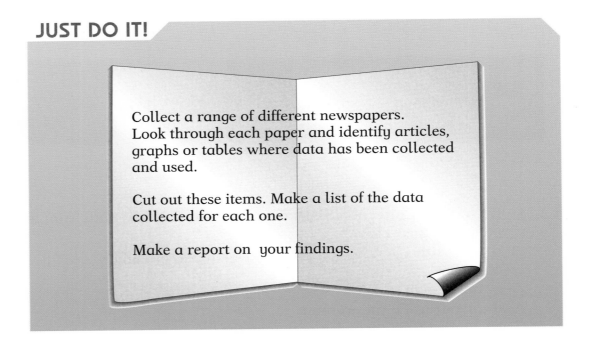

Collect a range of different newspapers.
Look through each paper and identify articles, graphs or tables where data has been collected and used.

Cut out these items. Make a list of the data collected for each one.

Make a report on your findings.

Use the Internet, books or newspapers as sources of secondary data to answer these questions.

7 Which country had the highest rainfall last year – England, Scotland, Wales or Ireland?

8 What were the crime figures in your area last month?

9 Which building society offers the best interest on a standard savings account?

10 Which TV soap had the highest viewing figures last week?

> **Primary data** can be collected using a questionnaire.
> The questions on the questionnaire must relate to the
> information you are collecting.

B 1 Julia is collecting data to find out which mobile phone is the
       most popular.

       Which of these questions are relevant and which are irrelevant?

       a Age?
       b Gender?
       c Make of current mobile phone?
       d How many sisters do you have?
       e How much did you pay for your mobile?
       f Which mobile would you buy if you had unlimited cash?

    2 Owen is collecting data to find out how much people spend on
       fast food.

       Which of these questions are relevant and which are irrelevant?

       a Age?
       b Gender?
       c What is your weekly income?
       d How often do you go on holiday?
       e Do you eat fast food?
       f How often do you visit a fast-food restaurant?

    3 Joel is collecting data to find out which career choices are the
       most popular.

       Which of these questions are relevant and which are irrelevant?

       a Do you eat sweets?
       b Which subjects are you taking at school?
       c Do you know what you want to do when you leave school?
       d Where did you go for work experience?
       e Have you had a Connexions interview?
       f Do you enjoy gardening?

    4 Write 3 relevant questions for each of these topics.
       a To find out the most popular sport and how much time people
          spend keeping fit.
       b To find out how much people spend on convenience foods.
       c To find out which supermarket gives the best value.

REVISION

Data you collect yourself is called **primary data**.

Data collected by other people, which you can find on the Internet, in tables and in reports, is called **secondary data**.

Primary data can be collected using a questionnaire. The questions on the questionnaire must relate to the information you are collecting.

LEARNING TIPS

Don't have more than 10 questions on a questionnaire unless you have to

You can use a Data Collection Sheet to collect data. You have to ask each person your questions and record them on your sheet

If you use a computer spreadsheet to record your data you can use ICT to help you sort the information

CHECK IT OUT

1   Give 3 topics you could use for a survey.

2   Which of these questions are relevant for Shahid's questionnaire?
    a   How old are you?
    b   Which hairdresser do you use now?
    c   Which dentist do you use now?
    d   How many times a year do you go to the hairdressers?

Survey to find the most popular hairdresser ...

ANSWERS

2a possibly   **b** relevant   **c** not relevant   **d** relevant

4.21 FREQUENCY TABLES AND DIAGRAMS

Frequency means how many.

A **1** Record this data in a frequency table like the one below.

Favourite fruit

apple	apple	strawberry	grape
banana	strawberry	strawberry	strawberry
grape	grape	banana	apple
strawberry	strawberry	banana	grape
apple	apple	strawberry	apple

Favourite fruit

Fruit	Tally	Frequency
apple		
banana		
grape		
strawberry		

Total _____

2 Record this data in a frequency table.

Favourite crisp flavour

CO	P	SV	SV	SV	P
SV	P	SV	CO	CO	CO
C	SV	CO	CO	CO	SV
C	SV	CO	P	SV	P

Key:
CO – cheese + onion
SV – salt + vinegar
C – chicken
P – plain

3 Record this data in a frequency table.

Favourite TV channel

Sky	ITV	ITV	BBC	Sky	BBC
BBC	ITV	ITV	C4	C4	C4
Sky	Sky	C4	ITV	C4	ITV
ITV	Sky	ITV	ITV	BBC	Sky
Sky	Sky	ITV	Sky	BBC	BBC

4 Record this data in a frequency table.

Favourite accompaniment to meat

pasta	rice	rice	pasta	pasta
rice	rice	pasta	rice	potato
potato	pasta	potato	potato	rice
pasta	pasta	potato	potato	potato
potato	potato	rice	potato	rice
potato	pasta	rice	rice	pasta

5 Record this data in a frequency table.

Favourite holiday destination

USA	Europe	Europe	Other	Europe
UK	USA	UK	USA	Europe
USA	UK	USA	USA	UK
Europe	Europe	USA	UK	Other
UK	Europe	UK	Other	USA

ß **1**

Make of car

Car	Tally	Frequency
Ford	⊬ |||	8
Audi	||||	4
Peugeot	⊬ |||	8
BMW	||	2
Volvo	⊬		6

This frequency table shows how many cars were in the car park, sorted into make of car.

a How many cars were in the car park in total?

b Which was the most frequent make?

c Which make of car had 2 cars in the car park?

An hour later 4 Peugeots left, 2 BMWs arrived and 3 Fords left.

d Draw a frequency chart to show how many of each make of car are now in the car park.

2 Sally recorded the first instrument played by the people in her GCSE music class.

Instruments played

Instrument	Frequency
piano	6
drums	2
guitar	3
voice	2
violin	8
flute	4
other	4

a How many people were in Sally's music class?

b What was the most popular instrument?

c How many more people played the piano than played the flute?

3 Greg collected data in a science experiment. He recorded the number of times each type of ball bounced when dropped from a given height.

Ball bouncing

Ball	Frequency
tennis ball	20
football	5
table tennis ball	22
squash ball	18
cricket ball	2

a Which ball bounced the least?

b Which was the bounciest ball?

c How many times more than the football did the table tennis ball bounce?

d What was the range of bounces?

JUST DO IT!

You need: a 10-sided dice

Roll the dice 50 times.
Record the number rolled each time in a frequency table.

Dice	Tally	Frequency
1		
2		
3		
⋮		

Compare your results with those of a friend.

Why are your results different?

FACT

The most common type of **frequency diagram** is a **bar-chart**.

JUST DO IT!

Use Microsoft Excel for this activity.

1 Input this table on a Microsoft Excel spreadsheet.

	A	B
1	Car	Cost per mile (p)
2	Jaguar X-Type	54
3	Rover 75	48
4	Toyota Corolla	32
5	Mazda 6	44
6	Renault Laguna	46
7	Ford Fiesta	31

You will need to make the columns wider.

2 Display the data in a variety of bar-charts.

C **1** Draw a bar-chart from this frequency table.

Survey to find people's
favourite radio station

Station	Frequency
Radio 1	15
Radio 2	3
Radio 3	0
Radio 4	2
Radio 5	5
Radio 6	1
local radio	11
other	3

2 Draw a bar-chart from this frequency table.

Survey to find which is the
most popular daily newspaper

Paper	Frequency
The Sun	12
The Mirror	5
The Daily Telegraph	12
The Times	4
local paper	7
other	10

3 Draw a bar-chart from this frequency table.

Survey of favourite films

Film	Frequency
horror	2
comedy	12
action	13
thriller	11
love/romance	9
animated	1
other	2

4 Draw a bar-chart from this frequency table.

Survey of sports injuries

Sport	Frequency
netball	3
football	22
rugby	2
hockey	11
other	2

5   In a water polo season the goal scoring of the key players was recorded. Matthew drew a bar-chart to show the results.

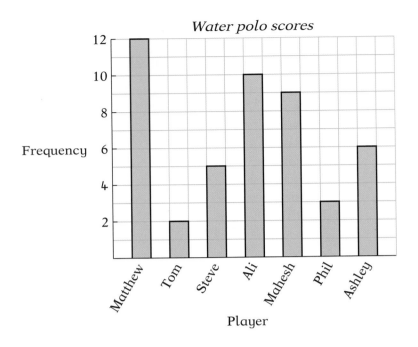

Draw a frequency table from this bar-chart.

6   The results of last year's Year 11 Maths GCSE have been recorded in a bar-chart.

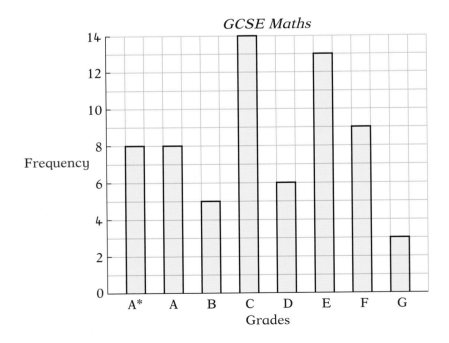

Draw a frequency table from this bar-chart.

7   This bar-chart shows the Key Stage 3 Maths SATS scores from
last year. It is split into boys and girls.

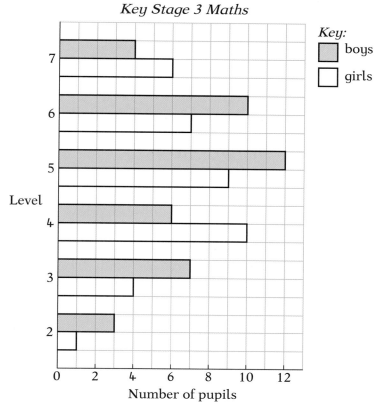

Key Stage 3 Maths

a Draw 2 frequency tables from this bar-chart. One for boys and
one for girls.

b Write down 2 differences between the boys' and the girls' results.

> When there is a large amount of data it can be sorted into
> **groups**.
>
> FACT

D   1   Jason carried out a survey to find out how many marks the
people in his class got in a test. He put the results into a grouped
frequency table.

Test marks

Mark	Tally	Frequency
1–4	||	2
5–8	|||	3
9–12	||||	4
13–16	ⅉ|||	8
17–20	||||	4

   a How many people were there in Jason's class?
   b Which group of marks had the highest frequency?
   c Which two groups had the same frequency?

2 Lena carried out a survey to find out how many marks the people in her class got in the same test.

Marks in test

3	6	19	9	8	19
9	14	14	6	10	14
5	15	7	9	14	19
14	17	10	16	15	
14	20	15	16	19	

   a Draw a grouped frequency table to show Lena's results.
   b How many people were there in Lena's class?
   c Which group of marks had the highest frequency?
   d Which group or groups had the same frequency as Jason's?
   e Which class had better results? Explain your answer.

JUST DO IT!

You need 2 6-sided dice.

1 Roll the 2 dice together 50 times and multiply the 2 numbers each time.

2 Record your results in a grouped frequency table.

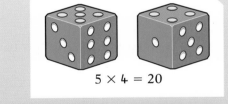

$5 \times 4 = 20$

Score	Frequency
1–3	
4–6	
7–9	
⋮	
33–36	
Total	**50**

REVISION

> **FACT**
>
> **Frequency** means how many.
> The most common type of **frequency diagram** is a **bar-chart**.

LEARNING TIPS

Make sure the scales on the axes of your frequency diagrams go up by regular amounts

Look at and use bar-charts and other frequency diagrams in other subjects such as geography, ICT or design technology

Use frequency tables and diagrams in your coursework

CHECK IT OUT

1. Record this data in a frequency table and then draw a bar-chart.

   Number of marks scored in a maths test (out of 10)

4	2	8	8	2	5	8	7
8	7	7	7	3	6	7	7
6	7	8	7	5	4	10	8

2. Put this data into a grouped frequency table.

   Number of marks scored in a maths test (out of 30)

26	28	19	17	27	15
25	20	12	28	30	16
12	15	18	22	27	24
11	21	15	24	25	21

ANSWERS

1

Score	Frequency
2	2
3	1
4	2
5	2
6	2
7	8
8	6
9	0
10	1
Total	24

Scores in a maths test

2

Score	Frequency
1–5	0
6–10	0
11–15	6
16–20	5
21–25	7
26–30	6
Total	24

4.22 PROBABILITY

Each number on a **fair** 6-sided dice has an **equal chance** of being rolled.

The probability of rolling a 4 is 1 out of 6.

$$\frac{1}{6}$$

A **1** Write down the probability of rolling each number on a 6-sided dice.

a

b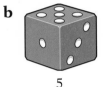

c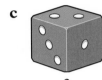

3   5   2

The top value is the number of **possible outcomes** for **a particular number**. → $\dfrac{1}{6}$

The bottom value is the **total** number of **possible outcomes**. →

2 Pia is rolling a 6-sided dice.
 a What is the total number of possible outcomes?
 b How many odd numbers are there?
 c What is the probability of rolling an odd number?

3 Eric is rolling a 6-sided dice.
 a What is the total number of possible outcomes?
 b How many numbers are less than 3?
 c What is the probability of rolling a number less than 3?

4 Stuart is rolling a 10-sided dice.
 a What is the total number of possible outcomes?
 b What is the probability of rolling a 2?
 c What is the probability of rolling a 9?
 d What is the probability of rolling a 5?
 e What is the probability of rolling an even number?
 f What is the probability of rolling a number less than 8?

5 Is the probability of rolling a 6 on a 6-sided dice greater or less than the probability of rolling a 6 on a 10-sided dice? Explain your answer.

6 There are 12 months in the year.
  a Write down all the months.
  b What is the probability that your birthday is in June?
  c What is the probability that a month chosen randomly has 8 letters?
  d What is the probability that a month chosen randomly has an 'a' in it?

> You can list all the **possible outcomes** in a table.
>
> FACT

Danny tosses a coin and rolls a 6-sided dice.
These are all the possible outcomes:

	1	2	3	4	5	6
Head (H)	1H	2H	3H	4H	5H	6H
Tail (T)	1T	2T	3T	4T	5T	6T

The probability of getting a Head and an even number is $\frac{3}{12}$.

There are **3** ways of getting an even number and a head.

There are **12** possible outcomes.

β **1** Copy and complete this frequency table to show all the possible outcomes from rolling 2 4-sided dice and adding the 2 numbers.

+	1	2	3	4
1	2		4	
2		4		
3				7
4		6		

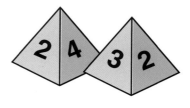

  a How many total possible outcomes are there?
  b How many even numbers are there?
  c What is the probability of scoring an even number?
  d How many 4s are there?
  e What is the probability of scoring 4?

317

f Is the probability of scoring 6 greater or less than the probability of scoring 7?

g Which scores have equal probability?

h Which numbers less than 10 are impossible to score?

2 Polly is dressing up.
She has 3 hats and 4 coats.

Draw a probability table or make a list to show all the possible outfits she could dress up in.

3 In a French restaurant the cost of a two-course meal is 10 euros.

Draw a probability table or make a list to show all the possible meals Darren could choose.

Plat Du Jour

Soupe
Melon
Paté

Poulé
Bifstek
Omellette
Canard

10 euros

REVISION

FACT

Each number on a **fair** 6-sided dice has an **equal chance** of being rolled.

The probability of rolling a 4 is 1 out of 6.

The top value is the number of **possible outcomes** for **a particular number**.

The bottom value is the **total number of possible outcomes**.

$$\frac{1}{6}$$

You can list all the **possible outcomes** in a table.

LEARNING TIPS

Total probabilities add up to 1. Check your answers add up to 1

Remember that the calculated probabilities don't always work out in real life

Work systematically when making lists of all the outcomes. Then you won't miss any out

CHECK IT OUT

1 What is the probability of rolling a 2 on a
   a 6-sided dice   b 4-sided dice   c 10-sided dice?

2 a List all the possible outcomes of rolling a 4-sided dice and tossing a coin.
   b What is the probability of getting a tail and a number less than 4?

EXAM PRACTICE 1

You need to copy parts of some questions before you answer.

1 **a** Write 3207 in words.

b Write fifty thousand and twenty in figures.

c Write 478 correct to the nearest ten.

d Write 4290 correct to the nearest thousand.

OCR, June 2001 (A), Paper 1

2 **a** What fraction of the diagram has been shaded?
Give your answer in its lowest terms.

b Make a copy of this diagram. Shade in extra sections so that,
altogether, $\frac{3}{5}$ of the diagram is shaded.

OCR, June 2001 (A), Paper 1

3 Tony sells trousers on Derby Market.
The table shows his sales last week.

Tony's trousers

Monday	🩳🩳🩳🩳	80
Tuesday	🩳🩳	35
Wednesday	🩳🩳	
Thursday	🩳🩳🩳	
Friday		30
Saturday		60

🩳 represents 20

a In the table, enter the numbers sold on Wednesday and
Thursday.

b Complete the table by drawing symbols to show the sales on
Friday and Saturday.

c Complete the bar chart to illustrate the information shown in the table.

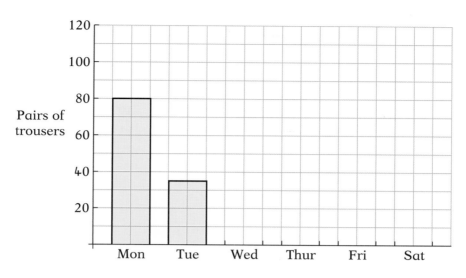

OCR, June 2001 (A), Paper 1

4 **a** Write down the mathematical name of each of these 3D shapes.

i 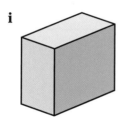   **ii**    **iii**

b Here is the net of a 3D shape.

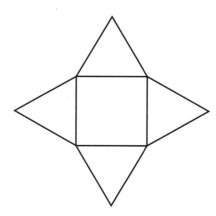

Write down the mathematical name of the 3D shape.

Edexcel, June 2000, Paper 1

5 "Clearview Double Glazing" sells three different types of window, each in two different sizes. They also sell doors and patio doors.

Type A		600 mm by 1050 mm	£65
		750 mm by 1200 mm	£80
Type B		1000 mm by 1000 mm	£85
		1250 mm by 1200 mm	£100
Type C		1200 mm by 1000 mm	£140
		1500 mm by 1200 mm	£170
Doors		**All sizes the same price**	£240
Patio Doors	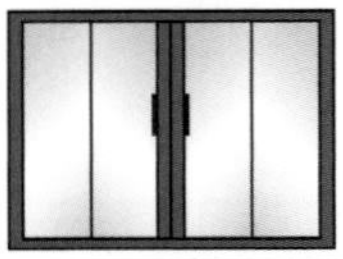	**All sizes the same price**	£550

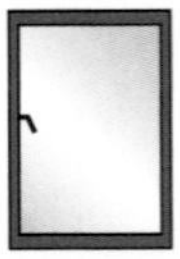

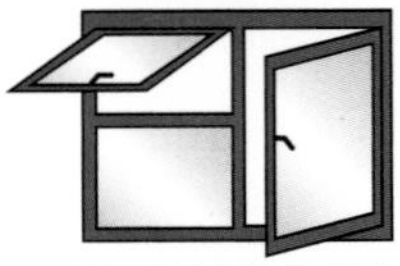

Work out the total charge for

2 Type A windows measuring 600 by 1050 each,

3 Type B windows measuring 1250 by 1200 each,

1 Type C window measuring 1500 by 1200 and

1 Patio door.

Show all your working.

OCR, June 2000 (A), Paper 1

6 A leaf is drawn below, full size, on a 1 cm grid.
Estimate the area of the leaf, stating the units of your answer.

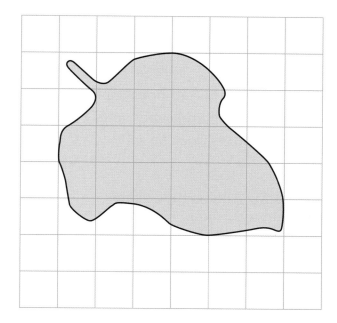

OCR, June 2000, Paper 1

7 Jackie counted the number of cars passing different places in 30 minutes. The pictogram shows her results.

shops	🚗 🚗
hotel	🚗 🚗
library	🚗 🚗 🚗 🚗 🚗
church	🚗 🚗 🚗
school	🚗 🚗 🚗 🚗 🚗 🚗 🚗 🚗 🚗

key: 🚗 = 10 cars

a How many cars passed the **school**?

b How many cars passed the **church**?

c 20 cars passed the shops.
Jackie counted 200 cars altogether.
What fraction of the cars passed the shops?
Give your answer in its simplest form.

AQA, June 2000, Paper 5

8 **a** A shopkeeper has 12 bags of nails.
In each bag there are 150 nails.
How many nails are there altogether?

b David buys 150 nails.
He uses 80% of the nails.
How many nails does he use?

c The shopkeeper has 45 boxes of bolts.
In one week the shopkeeper sells $\frac{2}{5}$ of the boxes.
How many boxes does he sell?

OCR, June 2001 (1664), Paper 1

9 Last month Mr Adams flew from
Birmingham to Lisbon.
His plane was due to take off
at 0850 and land at 1130.

a How long should his flight have taken?

His plane was delayed by $1\frac{1}{4}$ hours at Birmingham.

b At what time did his plane take off?

OCR, June 2001 (1664), Paper 1

10 Here are the first three patterns in a sequence.

pattern 1   pattern 2   pattern 3

a Draw the next pattern in the sequence.

b Copy and complete this table.

Pattern	1	2	3	4	5	6	7
Number of DOTS	4	6	8				
Number of LINES	4	7	10				

c Describe the sequence of the numbers
i   in the middle line of your table,
ii in the bottom line of your table.

d **Without drawing more diagrams**, find
i   the number of lines in pattern 12,
ii which pattern has 30 dots.   *OCR, June 2001 (1664), Paper 1*

11 This bar chart shows the number of grades A* to C that the students in form 11B obtained in their exams.

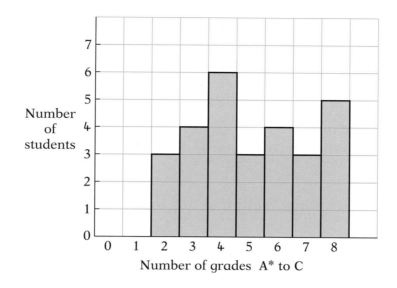

Number of grades A* to C

a How many students were there in form 11B?

b What fraction of the students obtained 5 or more grades A* to C?

OCR, June 2001 (1664), Paper 1

12 Margaret bought 24 books at £7.45 each.
Work out the total cost of these books.

OCR, June 2001 (1664), Paper 1

EXAM PRACTICE 2

1 **a** Write the number four thousand three hundred and sixty-seven in figures.

   b **i** Work out 2695 + 243.
      ii Work out 793 − 47.

   c Write the number 687 to the nearest 10.

   d The number 240 is divided by 10.
      What is the value of the 2 in the new number?

AQA, June 2000, Paper 5

2 **a** What name is given to this shape?

   b The diagram shows another shape.

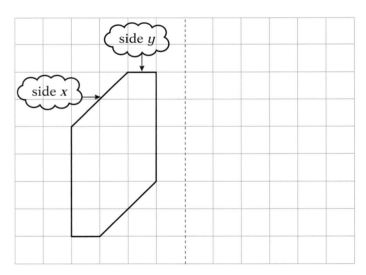

      i Put a cross (**X**) on the side **parallel** to side x.
      ii Put a circle (**O**) on a side **perpendicular** to side *y*.

   c Each square on the grid has an area of 1 cm².
      What is the area of the shape?

   d Reflect the shape using the dotted line as a mirror line.

AQA, June 2000, Paper 5

3   10 11 12 13 14 15 16 17 18 19 20

From the list of numbers above, select:

a an odd number

b a multiple of 7

c a square number

d a factor of 24

e a prime number

f the square root of 100.

OCR, June 2001 (A), Paper 1

4 The diagram shows part of a design.
The dotted lines are lines of symmetry of the whole design.
Complete the design.

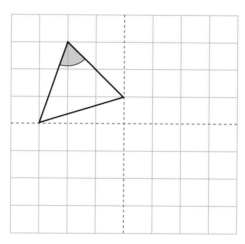

OCR, June 2001 (A), Paper 1

5   6 8 9 11 14 15 18 27

From the list of numbers above, write down:

a two numbers which add up to 20

b two odd numbers

c a multiple of 5

d the cube of 3

e a prime number.

OCR, June 2001 (1664), Paper 1

6 Dalbir conducted a survey on absence in his school.
He recorded the number of absences for each student for a term.

Here are the results for his form.

0	5	26	8	15	1	20	10
7	16	0	11	6	3	0	18
29	2	6	22	17	21	13	5
18	14	24	4	8	0	19	23

a Complete this frequency table for the results.

Number of absences	Tally	Frequency
0–4		
5–9		
10–14		
15–19		
20–24		
25 and above		

b i How many students were there in his form?

ii How many of these students had fewer than 20 absences?

OCR, June 2001 (1664), Paper 1

7 Debbie scored the following marks in five Science tests.

5   3   10   8   9

For these numbers, find:

a the mean,

b the median.

OCR, June 2001 (1664), Paper 1

8

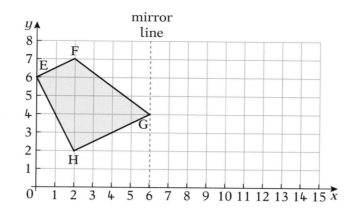

a Name two sides of the shape EFGH which are parallel.

b Mark clearly with a star (*) an obtuse angle in EFGH.

c Write down the coordinates of the point F.

d Reflect the shape EFGH in the mirror line.

OCR, June 2001, Paper 1

9 Write down the reading shown on this scale. Be as accurate as you can.

OCR, June 2001, Paper 1

10 The diagram shows patterns made from square tiles.

The numbers 2, 6, 12, 20, … form a number sequence.

Work out the eighth number in this sequence.

Diagram	Number of tiles
	2
	6
	12
	20

Edexcel, June 2000, Paper 1

11 **a** Here is a scale drawing of Brian's car in front of a fence.
       Brian's car is 4 metres long.

       Estimate the length of the fence.
       Give your answer in metres.

    b Brian stopped at a service station.
       He put petrol into his car.

       The diagram shows the petrol gauge
       in his car before and after he put the
       petrol in.

       i How many litres were in his car
           before he put the petrol in?

       ii About how many litres did
            he put in?

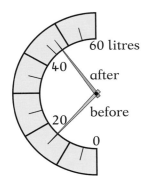

OCR, June 2001 (1664), Paper 1

12 Sarah bought two magazines which cost
    £1.95 and £1.39.

    a How much did they cost altogether?

    b She paid with a £5 note.
       How much change did she get?

OCR, June 2001 (1664), Paper 1

EXAM PRACTICE 3

1 a Write the number forty-five thousand six hundred and eight in figures.

 b Write your answer to part **a** to the nearest hundred.

Edexcel, June 2000, Paper 1

2 From the six words below, pick the correct four and write them in the boxes on the diagram.

diameter   arc   chord   tangent   radius   circumference

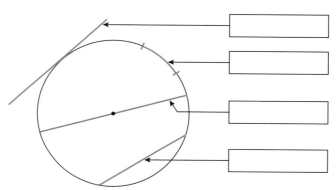

OCR, June 2000, Paper 1

3 a Write down all the factors of 20.

 b Write down the value of
   i 7^2
   ii $\sqrt{81}$

 c Here is a list of numbers:

   8   9   10   11   12   13   14   15   16   17   18

 From this list, select:
   i an even number
   ii a multiple of 6
   iii a prime number
   iv a cube number.

OCR, June 2000, Paper 1

4 John has five letters to post.

The weights of the five letters are 260 g, 150 g, 95 g, 235 g and 127 g.

a What is the median weight of the letters?

b The cost of posting a letter is given in the table.

Weight up to	First Class	Second Class
60 g	26 p	20 p
100 g	39 p	31 p
150 g	49 p	38 p
200 g	60 p	45 p
250 g	70 p	55 p
300 g	80 p	64 p
350 g	92 p	73 p

i The 95 g letter is sent by First Class post.

How much does this cost?

ii The 235 g letter and the 260 g letter are both sent by Second Class Post.

What is the total cost?

AQA, June 2000, Paper 5

5 Work these out.

a 52×9

b $328 \div 8$

c $5^2 \times 2^3$

d 127×23

OCR, June 2001, Paper 1

6 The diagram shows three angles meeting at a point.

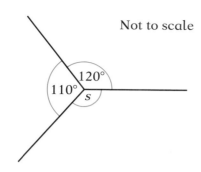

Not to scale

a What is the size of angle s?

b XY is a straight line.

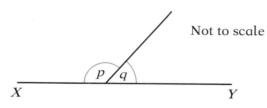

Not to scale

Angle q is 45°.

What is the size of angle p?

AQA, June 2000, Paper 5

7 a Solve the equation $10x = 360$

b Find the value of $2a + 3b$ when $a = 4$ and $b = 2$.

AQA, June 2000, Paper 5

8 Ian collected data on the food students bought in the school canteen. Here are his results.

Food	Frequency
Chips	12
Beans	5
Hamburger	10
Chicken curry	4

On the grid below draw a bar-chart to show this information.

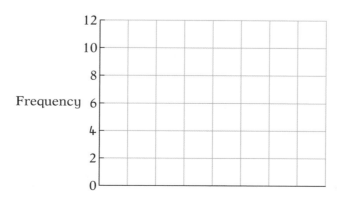

Edexcel, June 2000, Paper 1

9 **a** Reflect the triangle in the mirror line.

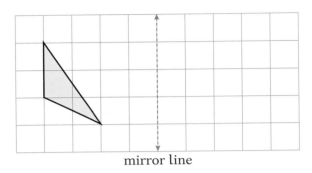

mirror line

b Rotate the triangle through 180° about centre A.

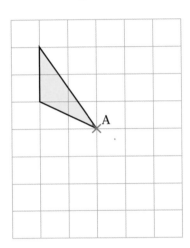

c Enlarge the triangle by scale factor 2, centre B.

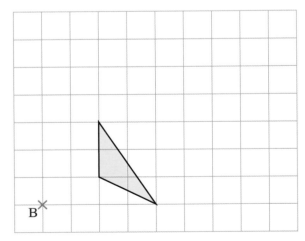

OCR, June 2000, Paper 1

10 On the probability line below, mark the following probabilities.

   i It will snow in London in June. Use the letter S.

   ii The sun will rise tomorrow. Use the letter R.

   iii A fair coin when tossed will come down heads. Use the letter H.

   iv A fair dice when rolled will show a five. Use the letter F.

Edexcel, June 2000, Paper 1

11 Work out.

   a 563×78

   b $793 \div 26$

Edexcel, June 2000, Paper 1

EXAM PRACTICE 4

1 **a** Write in figures, the number 'Eight thousand two hundred and nine'.

   b Work out
     i $326 + 147$ **ii** $326 - 147$

   c Write 2364
     i to the nearest 10,   **ii** to the nearest 100.

OCR, June 2000 (A), Paper 1

2

One evening last winter the temperature was:
 3°C in Cardiff
–4°C in Belfast
–10°C in Edinburgh.

   a Work out the difference in temperatures between
     i Cardiff and Belfast,
     ii Edinburgh and Belfast.

The temperature in Belfast increased by 6°C.

   b Work out the new temperature in Belfast.

The temperature in Edinburgh fell by 5°C.

   c Work out the new temperature in Edinburgh.

Edexcel, June 2000, Paper 1

3 **"What is your favourite group"?**

The bar-chart shows what some people said.

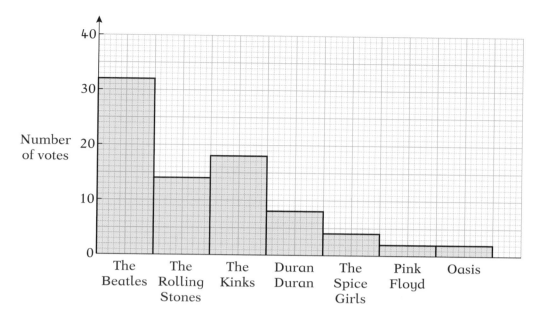

a Which group got 14 votes?

b How many people voted altogether?

c The information was collected between 10 o'clock and 11 o'clock on a Wednesday morning in Chesterfield market square.

Give two reasons why this was not a good way to collect the information.

Edexcel, June 2000, Paper 1

4 "Easymove Removals" make the following charges.

a Alice paid £270 to hire "Easymove Removals".
   For how long did she hire them?

b "Quickmove Removals" cost £36 per hour to hire.
   There is no fixed charge.
   Which is cheaper to hire for 5 hours, Easymove or
   Quickmove?
   You must show all your working.

AQA, June 2000, Paper 5

5 The diagram shows the net of a 3D shape.

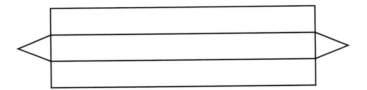

a Sketch the shape.

b What is the mathematical name of the shape?

c On squared paper, sketch a net of a cube.

OCR, June 2001, Paper 1

6

A theatre has 792 seats.
A pantomime is going to be performed 29 times.
All the tickets are sold.
Each ticket costs £10.

a i Do an approximate calculation to estimate how much money has been taken.

ii Is your estimate more or less than the actual amount of money taken?
Explain your answer.

b Calculate the exact number of tickets sold.

OCR, June 2000 (A), Paper 1

7 Ahmed has a set of square cards with numbers on them.

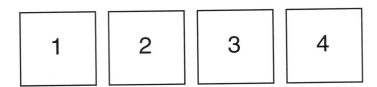

a Ahmed takes a square card at random.

What is the probability that he takes a 3?

Ahmed also has a set of circular cards with numbers on them.

b Ahmed takes a card at random from each set of cards.
He adds together the numbers on the two cards.

i Complete the table to show all the possible totals that
Ahmed can get.

□	1	2	3	4
4			7	
○ 5		7		
6	7			

ii What is the probability that Ahmed will get a total of 7?

AQA, June 2000, Paper 5

8 A marker board on the side of a harbour wall shows the water level.

One day. four readings were taken and the results were:

$$^-2, \ 5, \ 1 \ \text{and} \ ^-4$$

a Write these four readings in order starting with the **lowest**.

b How many metres are there between the highest and lowest of these four readings?

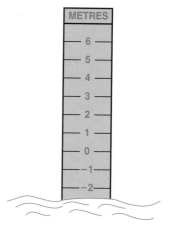

OCR, June 2001, Paper 1

9

These cards are placed face down on the table.
Sam picks one of the cards at random.

a Mark with a cross (✗), on the scale below, the probability of Sam picking a card with an even number on it.

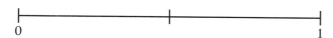

Explain your answer.

b Mark with a cross (✗), on the scale below, the probability of Sam picking a card with a number smaller than 7 on it.

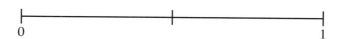

Explain your answer.

OCR, June 2001, Paper 1

EXAM PRACTICE 5

1 a Primitive apes first appeared on Earth thirty-five million years ago. Write this number of years in figures.

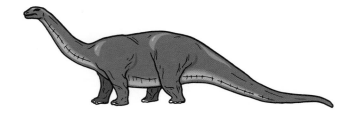

  b Dinosaurs first appeared on Earth 250 million years ago.
They died out 185 million years later.
How many years ago did they die out?

OCR, June 2001 (1664), Paper 2

2 Here is a list of numbers:

  4   10   6   24   12   22   36

  a Which of these numbers are factors of 30?

  b Find the biggest number that can be obtained by multiplying two numbers on the list.
You should not need to try all the possible pairs.

OCR, June 2001, Paper 2

3 Here is a pictogram.
It shows the number of people who had a meal in a café on each of four days.

Monday	⊕ ⊕ ⊕
Tuesday	⊕ ⊕
Wednesday	⊕ ⊕ ⊕ ◖
Thursday	⊕ ⊕ ⊕ ⊕ ⊕ ◹
Friday	

  ⊕ represents 20 people

  a Write down the number of people who had a meal in the café on

  i Monday,   **ii** Wednesday,   **iii** Thursday.

  On Friday, 55 people had a meal in the café.

  b Show this information on the pictogram.

Edexcel, June 2000, Paper 2

4 Write down the name of a unit which is used to measure

    i the length of a garden,

    ii the amount of petrol in a car's petrol tank,

    iii the area of a school playing field,

    iv the weight of a calculator.

Edexcel, June 2000, Paper 2

5

LADIES' JACKETS

70% Wool
30% Nylon

A jacket is 70% wool and 30% nylon.

a Write 70% as a decimal.

b Write 30% as a fraction.
    Give your answer in its simplest form.

c Write down the ratio of wool to nylon.

Edexcel, June 2000, Paper 2

6 Three friends had a meal together.
They had:

        3 'chef's specials' at £8.99 each
        2 drinks at £1.45 each
        1 drink at £1.75
        2 puddings at £2.49 each

They agreed to share the bill equally.
How much did they each pay?
Write down your calculations.

OCR, June 2001, Paper 2

7 Use this chart to answer the questions below.

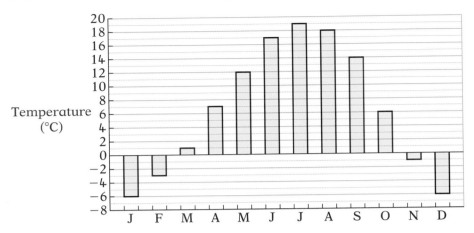

a What is the temperature in May?

b Which month is warmest?

c What is the temperature in February?

d For how many months is the temperature below zero °C?

e What is the difference in temperature (in °C) between January and June?

OCR, June 2000, Paper 2

8 For each shape in the table below state
   a how many lines of symmetry it has,
   b its order of rotational symmetry.

Shape	Number of lines of symmetry	Order of rotational symmetry

OCR, June 2001 (1664), Paper 2

9   Calculate the size of the angles *a*, *b* and *c*.

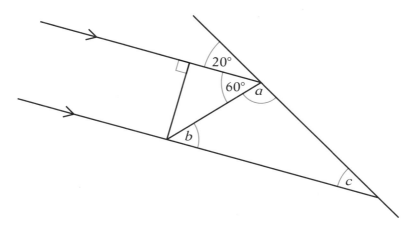

OCR, June 2000, Paper 2

10   There are 27 wall tiles in a pack.
Only full packs of tiles are sold.
A pack costs £9.72.

Barry needs 200 tiles.

a i   How many full packs of tiles
must he buy?

   ii Work out the total cost of these packs.

Each tile is a rectangle 20 cm by 15 cm.

b   Work out the area of one tile.

Navdeep wants to tile a wall.
The wall is a rectangle 3 metres by 2.4 metres.

c   Work out the number of tiles she needs to cover the wall
completely.

Edexcel, June 2000, Paper 2

11   Some students took part in a charity event.

They each had to carry as many bags of potatoes as they could across the school field in 15 minutes.

The results are shown in the bar-chart below.

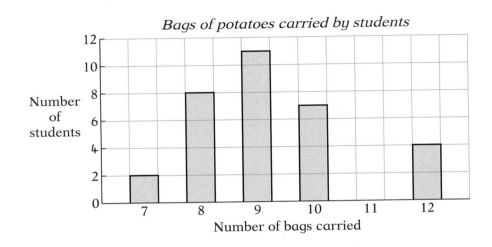

a   How many students took part?

b   What was the modal number of bags carried?

c   What was the range of the number of bags carried?

d i   What was the total number of bags carried?
   ii What was the mean number of bags carried?

OCR, June 2001, Paper 2

12 The cuboid below is made from a number of cubes identical to this one.

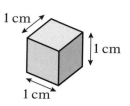

a Calculate the volume of the cuboid.

b The cuboid fits exactly into a box.
Copy and complete the net for this box.

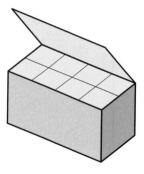

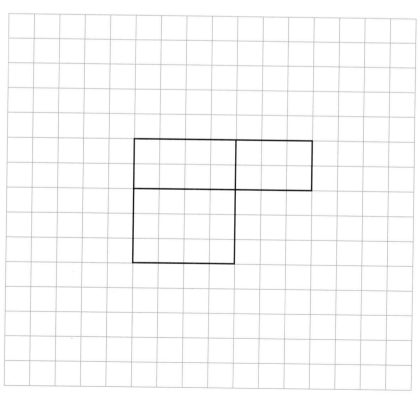

OCR, June 2001, Paper 2

EXAM PRACTICE 6

1

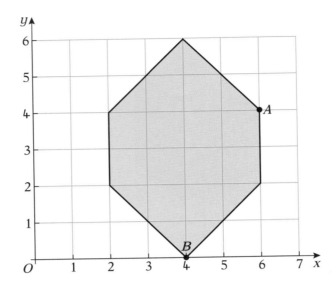

   a Write down the coordinates of point

     i A,

     ii B.

   b Work out the area, in square centimetres, of the shaded shape.

   c Measure the perimeter, in centimetres, of the shaded shape.

Edexcel, June 2000, Paper 2

3 The table below shows weather information for three cities in Scotland.

	Maximum temperature (°C)	Minimum temperature (°C)	Rainfall (cm)
Edinburgh	9	−2	7.8
Glasgow	11	3	11.5
Aberdeen	8	−4	6.9

a i Which city had the most rainfall?

   ii How much more rain fell in Edinburgh than in Aberdeen?

b Write down the minimum temperatures in order, with the lowest first?

c Find the difference between the maximum and minimum temperatures for Edinburgh.

d i Which city had the greatest range of temperature?

   ii What is this range?

e 1 inch = 2.54 cm.
How many inches of rain fell in Glasgow?
Give your answer to a suitable degree of accuracy.

OCR, June 2000, Paper 1

4 a Write down: the numbers which have 17 as a factor.

  b Write down: the numbers which do not have 17 as a factor.

     986   1129   493   789

OCR, June 2000, Paper 1

5 Ordinary marmalade is $\frac{3}{5}$ sugar.

    a What weight of sugar is there in
a 340 g jar of marmalade?

    b How much less sugar is there
in this 340 g of low sugar marmalade?

OCR, June 2000, Paper 2

6 **a**

> *JARS of COFFEE*
> *£2.79 each*
> *or* **3** *for the*
> *price of* **2**

    Jan, Kate and Lucy get together to buy 3 jars of coffee for the
price of 2.

    They divide the cost equally.

    How much does each one save on the normal price?

   b

    How many extra grams of marmalade do you get?

OCR, June 2000, Paper 2

7   The diagram shows a spinner.

There are four possible outcomes –
Blue (B), Yellow (Y),
Green (G) or Red (R).

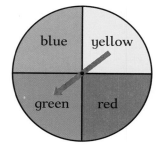

The spinner is spun 30 times.
The results are shown below.

G   Y   B   B   G   Y   B   Y   Y   Y
R   B   B   G   Y   B   R   B   Y   G
G   Y   B   Y   B   G   R   G   B   Y

a   Complete this frequency table.

Colour	Tally	Frequency
blue		
yellow		
green		
red		

b   Copy the axes below and draw a bar-chart to show this
information.

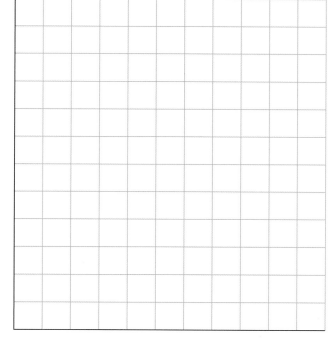

Frequency

c   The spinner is spun again. Which colour are you least likely to
get?

OCR, June 2001, Paper 2

8   1,   3,   5,   7,   9,   11,   13,   15,   ...

    a i What name is given to the numbers in this pattern?

      ii Write down the next two numbers in the pattern.

    b i Write down the next two lines in the following pattern.

$$1 = 1$$
$$1 + 3 = 4$$
$$1 + 3 + 5 = 9$$
$$1 + 3 + 5 + 7 = 16$$

....

....

      ii What name is given to the numbers in the right-hand column?

OCR, June 2000, Paper 2

9 'Start with a number, double it and then add one.'
Use this rule to fill in the boxes below.

$$0 \longrightarrow 1$$
$$1 \longrightarrow 3$$
$$2 \longrightarrow 5$$
$$3.5 \longrightarrow \square$$
$$5 \longrightarrow \square$$
$$\square \longrightarrow 15$$

OCR, June 2000, Paper 2

10

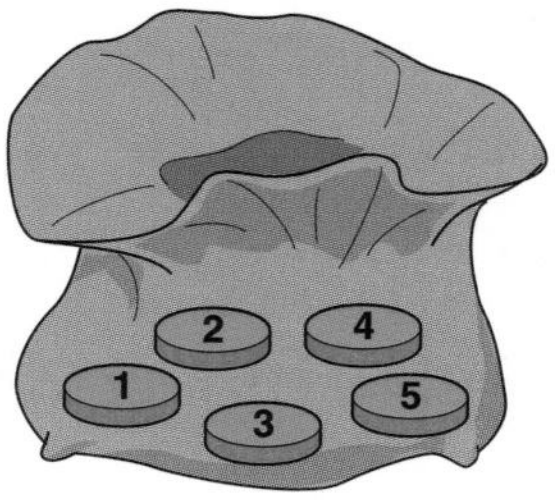

A bag contains five discs that are numbered 1, 2, 3, 4 and 5.
Rachel takes a disc at random from the bag.
She notes the number and puts the disc back.
She shakes the bag and picks again.
She adds the number to the first number.

a Copy and complete the table to show all the possible totals.

First number

	+	1	2	3	4	5
	1	2				
Second number	2					
	3				7	
	4					
	5					

b Find the probability that Rachel's total is

i 10,

ii 1,

iii 3 or 4.

OCR, June 2000, Paper 2

EXAM PRACTICE 7

1   6740 people watched a cricket match.
    a Write the number 6740 in words.
    b Write the number 6740 correct to the nearest hundred.
    c Write down the value of the 7 in the number 6740.

AQA, June 1999, Paper 2

2   **a** Write down the fraction of this shape which is shaded.

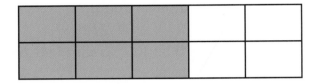

    b Shade $\frac{3}{4}$ of this shape.

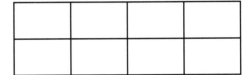

Edexcel, June 2000, Paper 2

3   Pat carried out a survey.
    She asked each pupil in her class how many postcards they received last August.

    Her results are shown in the vertical line graph.

    a What is the modal number of postcards received?

    b How many pupils took part in the survey?

    c How many postcards were received altogether?

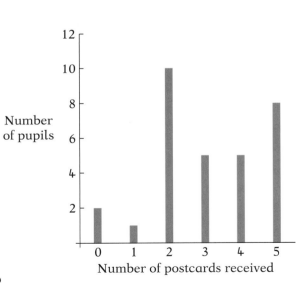

AQA, June 1999, Paper 2

4 Ben goes to a shop with £15 to buy 4 items.

He rounds each price to check if he has enough money.

Complete the table below to show what Ben might have done.

Item	Price (£)	
Coffee	2.85	
Meat	7.37	
Soap powder	3.50	
Sweets	0.45	

Does Ben have enough money?

Give a reason for your answer.

AQA, June 1999, Paper 2

5 £5 notes measure 7 cm by $13\frac{1}{2}$ cm.

The outline of a £5 note is shown on this centimetre squared grid.

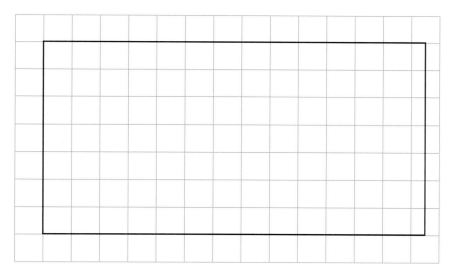

Not to scale

a Find the area of a £5 note.

b Find the perimeter of a £5 note.

OCR, June 2000, Paper 2

6 The River Amazon is 6437 km long.
How long is this

   a to the nearest 100 km,

   b to the nearest 10 km?

OCR, June 2000, Paper 2

7  An ordinary wine bottle holds 750 ml.
A display bottle holds the same as
20 ordinary bottles.

   a How much wine does the display bottle hold?

   b Write your answer to **a** in litres.

OCR, June 2000, Paper 2

8 Here is part of a spreadsheet.
It shows some number patterns arranged in columns.

   a Write down the two numbers hidden by the blots.

	A	B	C	D	E
1	1	1	2		
2	2	4	4		
3	3	7	8		
4	4	(i)	16		
5	5	13	32		
6	6	16	(ii)		
7	7	19	128		
8	8	22	256		

Number pattern/1

   b Describe the rule for continuing the pattern in column C.

OCR, June 2000, Paper 2

9 This grid shows the first three points in a pattern.

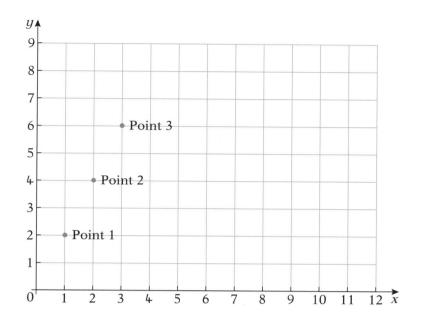

a Copy these axes and draw and label point 4 in the pattern.

b Copy and complete this table.

Point number	1	2	3	4
Coordinates	(1, 2)	(2, 4)		

c What are the coordinates of point 10?
Explain how you worked this out.

OCR, June 2001, Paper 2

10 This table shows the land-speed records since 1965.

Date of record	Car name	Record speed (m.p.h.)
2.11.65	Spirit of America	555.483
7.11.65	Green Monster	576.553
15.11.65	Spirit of America	600.601
23.10.70	The Blue Flame	622.407
4.10.83	Thrust 2	633.468
25.9.97	Thrust SSC	714.144
15.10.97	Thrust SSC	763.035

Use the table to answer these questions.

a What was the record speed of *Green Monster* to the nearest 10 m.p.h.?

b For how long did *Green Monster* hold the land-speed record?

c Which car was the first to travel at more than 600 m.p.h.?

d The first land-speed record was 39.24 m.p.h. How much faster is 763.035 m.p.h.?

e Which car broke the record on the 23rd of October?

OCR, June 2001, Paper 2

EXAM PRACTICE 8

1   From this list:

$$300\,\text{km}, \quad 300\,\text{m}, \quad 300\,\text{cm} \quad 300\,\text{mm},$$

choose the best one to complete each of the following sentences.

a A school ruler is .... long.

b The distance from London to Manchester is ....

c A school field is .... long.

AQA, June 1999, Paper 2

2   Complete the boxes in this subtraction.

$$
\begin{array}{ccccc}
 & 4 & 5 & 3 & 6 \\
- & 1 & \square & 8 & \square \\
\hline
 & 2 & 7 & 5 & 1 \\
\hline
\end{array}
$$

AQA, June 1999, Paper 2

3 The table gives information about five ski resorts on one day in December.

Ski resort	Temperature (°C)	Depth of snow (cm)	
		Lower slopes	Upper slopes
Aspen	−6	75	83
Cortina	4	25	110
Klosters	−8	35	190
Tignes	−3	90	120
Zermatt	0	20	90

a Write down the temperature in Tignes.

b Write down the depth of snow on the Lower slopes of Aspen.

The depth of snow on the Upper slopes in one of the resorts was 90 cm.

c Write down the name of this resort.

d Write down the name of the resort which had the lowest temperature.

e Write down the greatest depth of snow.
Give your answer in **metres**.

f How many degrees higher was the temperature in Cortina than the temperature in Aspen?

Edexcel, June 2000, Paper 2

4 a

Region	Number of countries in region
Africa	
Europe	
Asia	
Australasia and Oceania	
South America	
North and Central America	

Represents 4 countries

    i How many countries are there in South America?

    ii How many countries are there in Europe?

    iii There are 22 countries in North and Central America. Show this on the chart.

b This is an accurate scale drawing of the flag of Colombia.

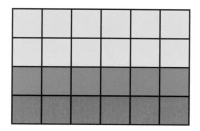

    What fraction of the flag is coloured blue?

OCR, June 2001, Paper 2

c i This table shows a tally of the colours used in 12 flags.
Copy the table. Complete the frequency column.

Colour	Tally	Frequency
red	ЖЖ ||||	
blue	ЖЖ |||	
green	||||	
yellow	ЖЖ ||	
white	ЖЖ ||	
black	|	

ii Here are some statements about these 12 flags.
Tick (✓) those which are right.
Cross (✗) those which are wrong.

Over 50% have yellow in them.

Less than $\frac{1}{10}$ have black in them.

One-third use green.

75% have red in them.

Less than half have white in them.

OCR, June 2001, Paper 2

5 a Copy and complete this bill.

0.8 kg of cheese at £4.75 per kg ....

1.4 kg of apples at 65p per kg ....

12 oranges at 14p each ....

TOTAL £ ....

b Mrs Jones pays this bill with a £10 note.
How much change does she receive?

OCR, June 2001, Paper 2

6 Two fair spinners are used for a game.
The score is the **difference**.

For example, the score for these two spinners is 6 − 4 = 2

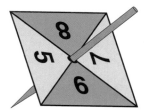 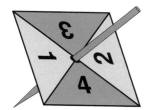

a Complete this table to show all
the possible scores for the two spinners.

b What is the probability of the
score being an odd number?

	5	6	7	8
1			6	
2	3			
3				5
4		2		

AQA, June 1999, Paper 2

7 Annie and Billy take part in a competition.
Annie fires at the target 10 times.

      8   8   9   5   6   6   5   8   8   6

a Work out

   i the range of her scores,   **ii** the mean of her scores.

The diagram shows a target.

Billy fires at the target 10 times.
The frequency table gives information
about his scores.

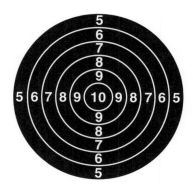

Score	Frequency
5	2
6	1
7	3
8	1
9	2
10	1

b Write down his modal score.

c Work out his total score.

Edexcel, June 2000, Paper 2

8 a Write down the coordinates of the point A.
  b Copy the axes and plot and label the points $B(-5, -2)$ and $C(1, 4)$.
  c Measure the distance AB.

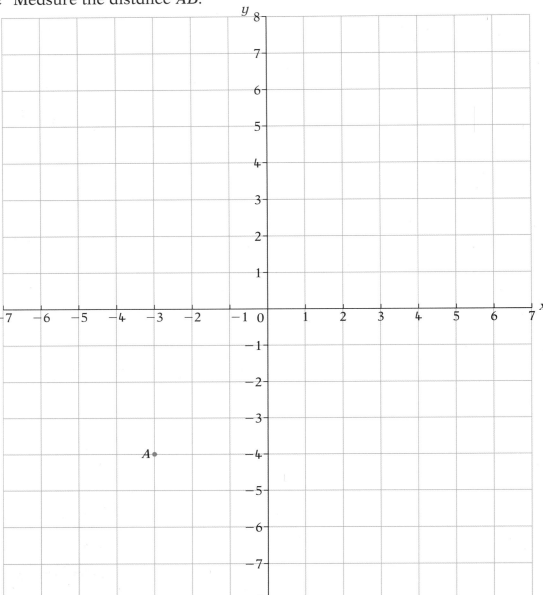

  d i Join A to B and B to C.
     ii Draw a line through A which is parallel to BC.
     iii Draw a line through C which is parallel to BA.
     iv Mark the point where these two lines cross and label it D.
  e What is the mathematical name for the shape $ABCD$?

AQA, June 1999, Paper 2

9 Look at this sequence. $\frac{1}{4}$, $\frac{2}{5}$, $\frac{3}{6}$, $\frac{4}{7}$, $\frac{5}{8}$, $\frac{6}{9}$, $\frac{7}{10}$,   ...
  a Write down the next two terms in the sequence.
  b Write down the 20th term in the sequence.
  c Which term in the sequence is equal to $\frac{2}{3}$?
  d Which term in the sequence is equal to 40%? *AQA, June 1999, Paper 2*